Preface

At the request of the United States Department of Agriculture and the Food and Drug Administration, the National Academy of Sciences, through a committee of the National Research Council, has examined the salmonella problem in the United States. This task was undertaken with the view of advising the USDA and the FDA on those aspects of the problem relating to their responsibilities in human and animal health. Particular attention is given to problems of control of salmonellosis as related to the food production and processing industries and to the activities of government in surveillance and research. Emphasis is also given to the need for broad educational activities and to the importance of control of salmonellae at the point where food is prepared for consumption. These latter activities are not, of course, the particular responsibilities of the USDA or the FDA, but they are so important in the control of salmonellosis that the Committee felt it useful to consider them.

The Committee has had the help and counsel of many scientists and administrators from industrial, governmental, and academic organizations. In addition, the USDA and the FDA have provided the Committee with a wealth of background information. These contributions are gratefully acknowledged.

The study was supported by funds made available under contract USDA 12–14–100–9467, administered by the Department of Agriculture.

iii

AN EVALUATION OF THE SALMONELLA PROBLEM

A Report of the
U.S. DEPARTMENT OF AGRICULTURE
and the
FOOD AND DRUG ADMINISTRATION,
U.S. DEPARTMENT OF HEALTH, EDUCATION, AND WELFARE

prepared by the
COMMITTEE ON SALMONELLA
DIVISION OF BIOLOGY AND AGRICULTURE
NATIONAL RESEARCH COUNCIL

NATIONAL ACADEMY OF SCIENCES
WASHINGTON, D.C.
1969

Publication 1683

Available from
Printing and Publishing Office
National Academy of Sciences
2101 Constitution Avenue
Washington, D.C. 20418

First printing, July 1969
Second printing, August 1970

Library of Congress Catalog Card Number 76–600461

Contents

I
INTRODUCTION, SUMMARY, AND RECOMMENDATIONS

1 Introduction

Salmonellosis of man is an important infectious disease in the United States. Its prevalence can only be estimated at this time, and it is certain that reported infections represent but a minority of the total number, because the fatality rate is low and the illness frequently mild and self-limited. Further, salmonellosis can not, except during epidemics, be accurately diagnosed on clinical grounds alone, and bacteriologic examinations are not usually undertaken. Finally, not all diagnosed cases are reported to health authorities. Infection frequently occurs sporadically and not in association with recognized food-poisoning outbreaks.

Salmonellosis may be caused by any of some 1,300 serotypes within the genus *Salmonella* including *S. typhi,* the agent of typhoid fever. Although typhoid has been brought under satisfactory control in the United States, infections by the other salmonellae have not. At the present time we must assume that all *Salmonella* serotypes are potential pathogens for man; yet it should be borne in mind that, over the years, serotype Typhimurium has been responsible for far more infections than any other serotype and that only 12 serotypes account for 78 percent of the documented human infections. It is salmonellosis due to serotypes other than *S. typhi* that is considered in this report.

In striking contrast to typhoid fever, the other salmonella infections occur naturally not only in man but in numerous other animal species as well. In man, these organisms are responsible for several distinct clinical entities, the most common being characterized by physicians as gastro-enteritis (or food poisoning). In a significant number of instances the organisms invade the bloodstream and give rise to salmonella fever or sepsis. They can also cause localized purulent infections, infections of the

1

urinary tract, and other clinical manifestations. Serious illnesses of these sorts are far more common in infants and in subjects with underlying disease than in older children and otherwise healthy persons.

Thus the problem of controlling salmonellosis in man is greatly complicated because of the widespread distribution of the organisms in the environment and the many ways by which they can reach the host. For example, the reservoir of salmonellae in domestic animals used as food for man means that raw foods of animal origin, particularly fresh pork and poultry, are likely to be contaminated when they reach the kitchen of home or restaurant. The problem is exacerbated by traditional slaughtering and handling practices that help to spread the contaminants from one carcass to another. The introduction of salmonella-contaminated products allows cross-contamination and spread of the organisms during food handling, even though the salmonellae in the original material may be killed during cooking.

Theoretically, this problem could be solved in either of two ways: eradicate salmonellae from domestic livestock, or train all food handlers in the proper ways to treat contaminated raw foods and require that those practices be followed. Clearly, the first alternative is impracticable at the present time, although much can be done to reduce the incidence of animal salmonellosis by improved management practices. The second alternative will require a massive educational program, and in any case it is unrealistic to rely on improved food-handling practices as the only protective measure.

Even if salmonellae could be eliminated from raw products of animal origin, person-to-person transmission would continue. Salmonellae can be spread from a case or carrier to susceptible individuals in many ways, including food contaminated during preparation. Numerous examples are available of the spread of salmonellosis in infant wards of hospitals following the introduction or development of the index case. No doubt the same thing occurs in family outbreaks. Scrupulous attention to sanitary practices by hospital employees, food handlers, and housewives is the only evident solution.

Recent experience has implicated a variety of processed foods and drugs (e.g., egg products, dry milk, coconut, inactive dry yeast, carmine dye, and thyroid powder) in outbreaks of salmonellosis. As a result, much attention has been paid to salmonella control in processed foods, and much progress has been made. For example, 20 years ago it was not uncommon to find tens of thousands of salmonellae per gram in dried egg products on the market. Recent experience indicates that salmonella contamination is far less frequent, and that when present the organism occurs at rates well below 1 per gram.

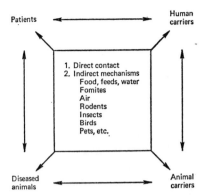

FIGURE 1 Possible routes of salmonellae transmission.

Although the foregoing examples do not cover all opportunities for man to contract salmonellosis, they suffice to illustrate the complexities of control. Figure 1 shows the many routes by which salmonellae can be transmitted.

Control of salmonellosis is not simply a matter of interrupting a cycle in nature. Elimination of salmonellae from animal feeds, for example, doubtless would go far toward reducing the incidence of infection in domestic animals but would not eliminate the disease. Improved food-handling practices, though badly needed, would not solve the problem of transmission in hospital wards. Thus, there is no simple or easy solution to the salmonellosis problem. To effect substantial reduction in incidence will require attack at many points along a broad front.

In devising a means to reduce the incidence of salmonellosis the greatest attention should be given to measures that can be expected to do the most good. Up to now, the emphasis has been directed toward processed foods that, though potentially hazardous, actually have been involved in relatively few outbreaks of disease. Examination of the salmonellosis incidents reported in 1967 shows the vast majority to be attributable to faulty food-handling practices, either in the home or in the food-service establishment.

This apparent misplacing of emphasis probably can be attributed to the nature of our regulatory control mechanisms. Control of contamination of food* in interstate commerce is the responsibility of the Food and Drug Administration, and that agency has exerted great pressure to eliminate salmonellae from such foods. Up to the present time, however, no

---

* In the context of the federal Food, Drug, and Cosmetic Act, "food" includes all articles used for food, drink, confectionery, or condiment by man or other animals. Accordingly, animal feeds and feed ingredients fall within the scope of the Act.

agency has devised adequate measures for controlling contamination of poultry and meat products on the market. Foods processed for intrastate sale, and food-service activities in general, are subject to control by state and municipal agencies which, with few exceptions, are inadequately equipped to exert salmonella controls. Thus, the most serious problem—mishandling of foods during preparation and serving—is the responsibility of the very agencies least prepared to handle it.

Reluctantly, we are forced to recognize the infeasibility of eradicating salmonellosis at this time. A great deal of improvement can be realized, however, through minimizing infection among domestic animals; better food handling practices; more careful attention to protection of processed foods; universal use of potable water for drinking, food processing and preparation, and cleaning food-processing and food-handling equipment; and better sanitary practices in kitchens, hospital wards, and similar places.

Meanwhile, in working toward the ultimate goal of eradication, several important problems must be solved. We need more precise information on the true incidence of the disease, both in man and in animals. More must be learned about the relationships between the pathogen and its host. We need to know how the animal (including man) becomes infected, the size of the infective dose, and the circumstances leading to the multiplication of the organisms, with and without overt disease. We need to know more about human-to-human, animal-to-human, and animal-to-animal transmission, about the ecology of the salmonellae in the intestinal tract, and about their interactions with other organisms. Implicit here is knowledge of the significance of the genetic variability or plasticity of the salmonellae and, in particular, the effects of antibiotics and other drugs in the organism's environment. It would be unfortunate, indeed, if the practice of feeding antibiotics to livestock resulted in development of salmonellae (or other pathogens) that are refractory to chemotherapy.

Readers of this report may sense an overemphasis on salmonella control in processed foods, with relatively too little said about mishandling of foods and the role of the human carrier. This simply is a reflection of (1) our present lack of a suitable mechanism to control mishandling and (2) our lack of knowledge of the role of the human carrier in transmission of the disease. The first deficiency can be corrected only by a massive educational program, the second only by research.

Clearly, adoption of well-planned and properly coordinated additional measures for the control of salmonellosis will aid in reducing other enteric infections of man.

In planning our review, the primary concern was with human health, and thus the review was organized around two viewpoints:

1. The disease: its importance, the causal organisms, and how man becomes infected

2. How man can be protected: through minimizing exposure by reduction of the incidence of animal salmonellosis, avoiding contamination of raw and processed foods, and bactericidal treatment and prevention of growth; through control by industry and regulatory agencies, including surveillance and investigation; through education; and through research

Finally, from the review there arose a group of recommendations for control of salmonellosis. These are set forth in the first Part of the report.

2   Summary

THE DISEASE

SERIOUSNESS OF THE PROBLEM

Salmonellosis is one of the most important communicable disease problems in the United States today. There are an estimated 2,000,000 human cases annually. In addition to the pain and suffering it causes, this disease is responsible for substantial costs in the form of medical care, hospitalization, and lost income through absence from work. Salmonellosis also causes substantial losses to the livestock and poultry industries through death of young animals, decreased milk and egg production, costly testing and control programs, and reduced value of contaminated products. Finally, the food-processing industry spends huge sums for testing and control programs, for remodeling plants and equipment, and for recall of contaminated products that are inadvertently placed on the market.

There is no way to measure accurately the total cost of salmonellosis to the American economy, but on the basis of a few known examples we consider the total cost to be at least $300 million annually, and probably more. As primarily a food-borne disease, salmonellosis is a potential threat to every resident of the country. Its prevention and control require the attention of the entire food-production, food-processing, and food-service industries, public health workers, regulatory agencies, physicians, hospital employees, veterinarians, laboratory personnel, and hosts of others, including the consumer himself.

6

THE CAUSAL ORGANISM

Salmonellosis is an infection caused by bacteria of the genus *Salmonella*. Their native habitat is the intestinal tract of animals, including man, but they are easily spread to other environments where they may survive and even multiply. When ingested by a susceptible host, the salmonellae can cause a variety of disease syndromes, or they may simply multiply without eliciting clinical signs of disease. Such "asymptomatic carriers" can spread the infectious agent just as effectively as an individual who is clinically ill.

The salmonellae can be divided into three groups on the basis of their host predilections:

1. *Primarily adapted to man.* This group includes *Salmonella typhi* and a few serotypes of *S. enteritidis* that are rarely found in animals other than man. Infections (e.g., typhoid and paratyphoid fevers) are characterized by a prolonged incubation period (10 to 20 days or more), generalized disease with bloodstream invasion (as opposed to acute enteritis), and a tendency to produce carriers and to become endemic. Public health measures have succeeded in bringing diseases caused by organisms of this group under control.

2. *Primarily adapted to particular animal hosts.* Included in this group are several important pathogens of domestic animals, such as *Salmonella cholerae-suis* and serotypes of *S. enteritidis*—Pullorum, Gallinarum, Dublin, Abortusequi, Abortusovis, and Typhisuis. These organisms can all cause gastroenteritis in man, although serotype Dublin and *S. cholerae-suis* are the most important in this respect. Infections by the latter may be quite severe, particularly in children.

3. *Unadapted.* This group includes some 1,300 distinct serotypes of *S. enteritidis* that seemingly attack man and other animals with equal facility and with no evident host preference. In man, the disease typically consists of gastroenteritis beginning 6 to 24 hours after ingestion of the organisms. Infection is localized in the intestine, and blood stream invasion is not uncommon. The usual vehicle is contaminated food. Although many hundreds of unadapted serotypes are known, 96 percent of the cultures isolated from man and animals belong to only 55 serotypes.

The large number of antigenically distinct serotypes, and the ease with which mutants can be obtained experimentally, has led to the supposition in some quarters that the salmonellae possess an unusual degree of "genetic plasticity." There is no sound basis to conclude that these organisms undergo genetic change to any greater or lesser degree than other members of the Enterobacteriaceae, or for that matter, other groups of bacteria. The salmonellae exhibit the usual mechanisms of genetic recombination (e.g., transduction, phage conversion, conjugation), and they readily give rise to mutants, but there is no evidence that the disease-producing capacity or other fundamental characteristics of the mutant progeny are significantly different from those of the parent cells.

The observation that multiple drug resistance can be transferred to salmonellae from *Escherichia coli* and possibly other intestinal microorganisms has raised questions about the safety of feeding antibiotics to domestic animals for stimulation of growth. The potential hazard of this practice has been demonstrated by observations that (1) antibiotic therapy in hospitals has led to a greatly increased incidence of antibiotic resistance among salmonellae isolated from patients; and (2) prophylactic and therapeutic use of antibiotics to control disease in calves has led to an increased incidence of antibiotic-resistant salmonellae in England. Thus there is evidence that widespread use of antibiotics is, indeed, increasing the drug resistance of the salmonella population in selected environments.

Antibiotic resistance may have little importance in regard to salmonella gastroenteritis because these infections, when limited to the intestinal tract, are not usually responsive to antibiotics. Treatment of infections in other parts of the body (e.g., bloodstream, urinary tract) would be seriously complicated, however, if the causal organisms were resistant to antibiotics and other therapeutic agents.

HOW MAN BECOMES INFECTED

Most salmonella infections begin in the intestinal tract following ingestion of the causal organism. In recognized outbreaks the usual vehicle is contaminated food. However, in the far more common sporadic cases and family outbreaks the vehicle is rarely identified. Both in these and in many hospital-associated outbreaks, particularly in infant wards, there is convincing evidence of person-to-person or person-to-fomite-to-person transmission, thus emphasizing the importance of personal hygiene in salmonella control.

Owing to the high frequency of salmonella infections in domestic animals, foods of animal origin (e.g., egg, meat, and poultry products) are the ones most likely to carry the organisms. Fruits and vegetables are usually free of salmonellae unless they are produced or handled in a contaminated environment. Processed foods, though not often involved in outbreaks of salmonellosis, may carry the organisms if they contain a contaminated ingredient (such as contaminated dried eggs, dried milk, or coconut), if the processing treatment is inadequate, or if they become contaminated after processing.

Foods also may be contaminated by food handlers who are excreting salmonellae or by rats, mice, insects, and other vermin. Cross-contamination from raw material to finished food by hands, utensils, or work surfaces is another hazard both in the kitchen and in the processing plant.

Water is not a frequent vehicle of salmonellosis owing to the efficacy of modern water treatment processes. Untreated water supplies may be contaminated, and surface waters not uncommonly contain salmonellae. The likelihood is greatest, naturally, where human and animal wastes are found.

Pharmaceutical and enzyme preparations from animal organs represent a special problem. The raw materials are commonly contaminated with salmonellae, and the organisms may not be eliminated during processing since, in order to preserve the desired biological activity of the products, only relatively mild bactericidal treatment can be used.

Of the many routes by which man can acquire salmonellosis, special mention should be made of household pets, including dogs, cats, turtles, chicks, and ducklings. Many outbreaks, particularly among children, have been traced to these sources.

HOW MAN CAN BE PROTECTED

There are two ways to protect against infection: prevent exposure to the pathogen or immunize the host. Immunization against typhoid has long been practiced, but there is no evidence that immunization would have practical value against salmonella gastroenteritis. Therefore, current control procedures are aimed at preventing exposure, i.e., keeping salmonellae away from the potential victim.

Better care and sanitation in the home, nursery, hospital, and food-service establishment would no doubt reduce the incidence of salmonellosis, but the problem can not be eliminated as long as our foods are contaminated with the organisms. Although it is unreasonable in the foreseeable future to expect eradication of salmonellosis, a great deal can be done to reduce the incidence of salmonellae in our food supply and thereby minimize the likelihood of infection. To do this, salmonellosis in domestic animals and contamination of foods during processing must be controlled, and salmonellae in raw products must be destroyed and their growth prevented by processing. Regulatory, surveillance, and educational procedures must be developed for and applied to the task, and new knowledge for use in salmonella control must be generated by research.

CONTROL OF SALMONELLOSIS IN DOMESTIC ANIMALS

Animals acquire salmonellosis much as man does, via feed and water and by direct contact with contaminated materials or other animals. As is true for man, animal salmonellosis is most severe in the young, whereas mature animals are more likely to develop inapparent infections and to become asymptomatic carriers of the organisms. These animals offer the greatest potential hazard to public health because they are the ones most likely to enter the human food supply undetected.

Traditional animal husbandry practices allow ample opportunity for the spread of salmonellosis within flocks and herds, but certain modern innovations are likely to exacerbate the situation. For example, increased use of contaminated animal by-products to feed poultry and swine (e.g., meat and bone meal, fish meal, and poultry meal) exposes more animals to infection; and greater crowding of animals into feeding lots, broiler houses, and holding pens increases the likelihood of spread from one animal to another. No less significant is the long-standing practice of crowding animals together in vehicles during transportation and holding them in dirty pens while awaiting slaughter. Numerous studies have demonstrated the rapid spread of salmonellae under these circumstances.

To eradicate salmonellosis from domestic animals will require radical and very expensive changes in management practices all the way from breeding to slaughter; it is therefore unreasonable to expect complete elimination of all salmonella infections in the foreseeable future. However, a great deal of improvement could be made simply by adherence to well-known principles of disease control. For example, the following steps would go a long way toward reducing the incidence of salmonellae in domestic animals:

1. Minimize salmonella-contaminated feeds, giving special attention to animal by-products used largely for feeding poultry and swine.

2. Convert the present pullorum and fowl typhoid control programs into eradication programs involving all chicken and turkey breeding flocks.

3. Develop salmonella-free breeding herds and flocks, and protect them against contamination from outside sources.

4. Provide clean water supplies and hold animals in sanitary buildings and pens.

5. Segregate clinically ill animals and withhold them from the market as long as they are excreting salmonellae.

6. Schedule shipment of animals to permit holding them on the farm as long as possible and at the slaughterhouse for as short a time as possible.

7. Transport animals to market in clean vehicles.
8. Hold animals at the slaughterhouse in clean pens or cages.

CONTROL OF CONTAMINATION IN FOOD PROCESSING

Food processing takes many forms. It may range from simple blending and packaging of dry ingredients (e.g., cake mix) to a succession of processing steps including a bactericidal treatment (e.g., ready-to-eat cured meats). Each process must be examined in terms of the nature of the raw materal and the treatment it receives during processing. In any event, the processor must ensure against the addition of salmonellae from the processing-plant environment. This precaution involves nothing more than adherence to time-honored principles of sanitation and good manufacturing practice.

Even with frequently contaminated foods (e.g., poultry and meats) the number of individual animals carrying salmonellae is usually relatively small. Unfortunately, however, many slaughtering procedures provide very effective means of spreading contamination from infected to clean carcasses. Correcting this problem will require substantial changes in slaughterhouse methods.

Similarly, a few contaminated eggs can contribute salmonellae to large quantities of clean eggs during blending for freezing or drying. Salmonella control thus depends on effective pasteurization of the liquid egg before further processing.

Most dry blending operations (e.g., gelatin desserts) do not include an effective bactericidal treatment; hence, control depends on the use of clean ingredients.

Whatever the process, care must be taken to avoid reintroduction of salmonellae by contaminated equipment or by airborne dust.

DESTRUCTION OF SALMONELLAE AND PREVENTION OF GROWTH

When a food product (e.g., poultry, eggs, meat) is naturally contaminated with salmonellae, the only protection for the consumer lies in a bactericidal treatment. With fresh meat and poultry this step takes place when the food is cooked for the consumer. With processed eggs, ready-to-eat meats, milk, and similar items it is done in the processing plant, usually by heat.

Fortunately, in most foods salmonellae are easily killed by heat. The effectiveness of a given heat treatment depends on several factors, including, especially, the available water, pH, and number of organisms to be killed. Therefore, any bactericidal treatment considered for a particular product must be evaluated in terms of the composition of the food. Products containing high concentrations of sugar, for example, require more rigorous treatment than products with little sugar.

Salmonellae should not be allowed to grow in a food product at any time. Large numbers of the organisms increase the likelihood that some will survive the bactericidal treatment, if one is used, and also the hazard to personnel working in the plant. Prevention of growth involves the application of well-established bacteriological principles concerning pH, available water, temperature, and similar factors.

Vigorous pursuit of the foregoing steps—i.e., reducing the incidence of salmonella infections in domestic animals and adherence to good manufacturing practices in food processing—should go far to ameliorate the salmonellosis problem but will not eliminate it entirely. The effectiveness of these steps can be measured only in terms of reduced incidence of salmonella-contaminated foods on the market and on reduced incidence of human salmonellosis as reported to the U.S. Public Health Service.

Inherent in any effective system for prevention of salmonellosis are the activities of three groups: the food-processing industry, regulatory agencies, and surveillance agencies.

INDUSTRY CONTROLS

Serious and widespread efforts to prevent the sale of salmonella-contaminated foods in this country have been in effect for less than three years and have been applied only to certain products in interstate commerce. Existing control measures were established by the Food and Drug Administration on the grounds that salmonella contamination constitutes adulteration. Meat and poultry products have not been subjected to the same degree of scrutiny.

The initial thrust of regulatory activities has been made at products known to be responsible for outbreaks of salmonellosis (e.g., processed eggs, nonfat dry milk, inactive dry yeast, carmine dye) and has been expanded to products in which these materials serve as ingredients (e.g., noodles, candy, milk chocolate). Presence of salmonellae has been considered grounds for recall of the product from the market.

Of necessity, and perhaps properly, food processors have responded to regulatory pressure by vastly increasing their efforts to avoid salmonella contamination in their products. Large sums of money are being spent for testing raw materials and finished goods and for monitoring the environment of the processing plant. Coincidentally, the regulatory agencies, especially the FDA, have increased the scope of their testing programs for products on the market.

Whether the current monitoring programs of industry and the regulatory agencies have caused significant reduction in the incidence of human salmonellosis is unknown. There are ample reasons to believe that mishandling of foods in the home and in food-service establishments is far more significant in human salmonellosis than are processed foods such as candy or even dry milk.

We can not condone the sale of foods containing salmonellae, but at the same time we must recognize that salmonellae can be found in many products if a sufficient number of tests are made. Therefore, one may ask: When should we stop testing and conclude that a product is salmonella-free (which may simply mean that the contamination level is below the sensitivity of the test procedure)?

The lack of a definitive sampling and testing procedure has caused confusion and uncertainty in the food-processing industry. Basically, a food processor wants to know if a given lot of material is safe to ship. How much testing must he do before he can conclude that the product is neither a hazard to health nor likely to be seized by a regulatory agency?

No one knows the minimal infective dose of salmonellae. We know that it varies with serotype, strain, and host. It is safe to conclude that a single salmonella cell offers greatest hazard if it is in a product that will allow growth before consumption or in a product intended for the most susceptible consumers (e.g., infants, the aged, and the infirm).

Therefore, in assessing the potential salmonella hazard of a given product, we believe its ultimate use should be taken into consideration. Is the product likely to be consumed without cooking or other bactericidal treatment? Is there likely to be opportunity for growth before consumption? Is the product intended for individuals in the more susceptible segments of the population?

In Chapter 10, we have suggested a sampling and testing scheme that will, we believe, relieve much of the uncertainty faced by food processors today and at the same time afford ample protection against distribution of processed foods containing significant levels of salmonellae. We are not recommending finite tolerances *per se*. Rather, on the basis of knowledge now available, we believe that salmonella levels too low to be detected by the proposed procedure entail relatively little health hazard to the consumer. For this proposal to be of value it obviously must be acceptable to both regulatory agencies and food processors.

There is no way to be absolutely sure that a given lot of food is salmonella-free in the absolute sense without testing every gram of it. Nevertheless, we believe the proposed sampling and testing plan will give ample protection.

REGULATORY CONTROLS

Regulations do not prevent salmonellosis, but the incidence of the disease could be reduced significantly if suitable regulations were adopted and enforced. At the present time, many regulatory agencies are involved at different levels of government with varying degrees of effectiveness.

The Food and Drug Administration, with primary concern for the consumer's safety, enforces the provision of the Food, Drug, and Cosmetic Act that bans the distribution of adulterated foods in interstate commerce. Salmonella contamination to any detectable degree is regarded as adulteration. The agency has no jurisdiction over products that are manufactured and sold intrastate.

The U.S. Department of Agriculture is primarily concerned with the welfare of the farmer, but it is also responsible for supervising the slaughter and processing of meat and poultry. Animal-disease prevention is a major part of its activity, and the inspectional procedures at slaughterhouses are designed to prevent the use of diseased animals for human food. Yet these inspections do not include the detection of salmonellae on meat and poultry.

Some state agencies, usually the departments of agriculture or public health, inspect food-processing plants and enforce regulations covering safety and wholesomeness of foods produced within their jurisdictions. In general they tend to follow the procedures of the federal regulatory agencies (FDA and USDA), but practices vary widely from state to state. In addition, many state boards of health inspect restaurants, hotels, institutions, and other food-service establishments, although such inspection rarely includes measures that would be effective in preventing salmonellosis.

A very few large municipalities and some counties maintain inspection and laboratory facilities that function as described for state agencies. However, most municipalities do little that is effective in prevention of salmonellosis.

As might be expected with so many different agencies involved, there are areas of overlap and areas with little or no supervision. Both the FDA and the USDA and some state agencies inspect egg-processing factories, milk-drying plants, and rendering establishments with particular attention to salmonella control. Yet no agency seemingly has given active attention to the presence of salmonella-contaminated meat and poultry products on the market.

Of probably even greater importance in the prevention of human salmonellosis is the woefully inadequate supervision of mass-feeding operations including caterers, restaurants, hotels, delicatessens, institutions, and schools. State and municipal inspectors, when available at all, seem to be more concerned with what they can see (e.g., hairnets on employees and window areas in kitchens) than with salmonellosis.

With the historical precedent of multiagency jurisdiction and the general reluctance of state officials to welcome federal intervention, we are hesitant to recommend that a single agency should be charged with control of salmonellosis throughout the country. At the very least, however, there should be closer coordination and exchange of information between the several federal agencies and between state and federal organizations to assure a minimum of overlapping of their activities and to eliminate gaps in regulatory coverage. In particular, and in view of the rapidly growing trend of Americans to eat away from home, we urge that closer attention be paid to salmonella control in mass-feeding establishments.

It is clear that none of the agencies is equipped to do all it should be doing toward salmonella control. The deficiency is most acute at the state and local levels where, in our view, the need is greatest.

SURVEILLANCE

Though not a control measure itself, surveillance is an essential adjunct to any control system designed to prevent or minimize salmonellosis. Surveillance is necessary to know the magnitude of the problem, to indicate areas where investigation is necessary, and to measure the effectiveness of corrective measures. The salmonella surveillance program of the United States, though admittedly inadequate, already has demonstrated the seriousness of the salmonella problem in public health. Moreover, by virtue of clever epidemiological work, it has revealed certain vehicles for salmonellae (e.g., nonfat dry milk) that were not previously suspected. Thus continual surveillance is necessary to provide warnings of potential hazards, to explain the sources of outbreaks, and to provide a measure of effectiveness of control procedures instituted by industry and governmental agencies.

If all foodstuffs could be freed of contamination, if everyone drank and swam in potable water, and if all carriers could be cleared of salmonellae, human salmonellosis would virtually disappear. This ideal obviously is not in prospect, and man must learn to live with salmonellae for many years to come.

EDUCATION AND TRAINING FOR PREVENTION OF SALMONELLOSIS

A great deal has already been done to focus the attention of the food-processing industry, and to some extent the food-service industry, on the seriousness of the salmonella problem. Effectiveness has been greatest where regulatory pressure was applied. However, the vast majority of the public and personnel of the various food-associated industries barely know that salmonellae exist. Many of them have suffered from salmonellosis, but they do not know why or how to avoid future incidents.

With salmonellae in the environment as they are now, significant progress in reducing the incidence of human salmonellosis will require a massive educational campaign directed at personnel of the food-processing, food-distribution, and food-service industries, farmers, and even housewives. Equally critical is the education of physicians and veterinarians to the importance of recognizing and reporting cases of salmonellosis and of hospital personnel in preventing the spread of salmonellae among patients.

In view of the many facets of the salmonella problem and the large numbers of people to be informed, we believe the federal government should institute a broad continuing program using all appropriate communications media to inform the public about ways to prevent salmonellosis.

RESEARCH

Finally, for the long-term effective control of salmonellosis, much remains to be learned about the biology of the organism, host susceptibility, epidemiology, and the application of control measures.

3 Recommendations

Insofar as practicable we have grouped our recommendations around the major problems that relate to prevention of salmonellosis: contamination of raw food products and drinking water; contamination of processed foods, feeds, and drugs; and mishandling of foods during preparation and serving.

Education is an essential part of all control programs, and for this reason we have assembled the recommendations for education and training in one group.

Finally, truly effective control of salmonellosis will require information that is not now available; hence, our recommendations for research are in one group.

1. Contamination of Raw Animal Products and Drinking Water

(a) Steps should be taken toward universal participation in a salmonella-control program for poultry flocks and other livestock, concentrating on the prevalent serotypes first. Educational and regulatory programs are required to make this recommendation effective. Assistance should be given by educational institutions and regulatory agencies to improve and implement better controls in husbandry practices, including feeding and management programs designed to eliminate or reduce salmonella infection or contamination in poultry flocks and in other livestock. Educational programs should stress the benefits to the producer that result from a salmonella control program.

(b) An eradication program should be developed for pullorum disease and fowl typhoid involving all chicken and turkey breeding flocks in the United States.

(c) Buildings and equipment for domestic animals should be designed and constructed so that they can be easily and thoroughly cleaned and sanitized.

(d) Regulations that require the reporting of animal infections due to *Salmonella* serotypes should be developed.

(e) The use of truly low levels of antibiotics in feeds for promotion of growth of animals should be permitted until and unless it is proved that these levels are not safe for the consumer and so long as genetic changes of the microbial organism occur at an acceptably low rate. The use of higher levels for prophylactic purposes should not be permitted. This recommendation is not intended to preclude therapeutic applications of drugs in the control of animal disease.

(f) Although salmonellae in raw food commodities such as shellfish, fruits, meats, and poultry are destroyed by adequate cooking or other sterilizing procedures, these foods are frequently not adequately cooked before consumption. They should be subjected to the same careful surveillance as now pertains to processed foods. It is therefore recommended that existing legislation concerning control be implemented, and, if inadequate, that study be initiated to develop adequate regulatory measures and to delegate responsibility for enforcing them.

(g) Community-drinking-water supplies should be chlorinated, if necessary, to ensure freedom from salmonellae.

2. Contamination of Processed Foods, Feeds, and Drugs

(a) Federal agencies should establish formal collaborative and cooperative agreements to fill gaps in control programs and to avoid duplication of effort, of regulations, and of inspections. Public health agencies should be included in these agreements.

(b) Similar formal agreements should be established between federal and state agencies, and among state agencies, to maintain uniformity of standards. Effective relationships should be established that will permit a strengthening of state responsibilities and authority and enable the development of effective working relationships with the food industries.

(c) Federal and state agencies should develop and implement programs to control salmonella contamination of feeds and feed ingredients. Federal and state laws should be comparable for administration of acceptable state and national programs. Regulations should define inspection responsibilities and interagency relationships. Examples of important considerations include terminal pasteurization of animal by-products, protection of animal feeds or feed ingredients from recontamination by rodents, birds, and other wild animals or insects, and provision of clean, sanitized carriers and prevention of common transportation with other products in trucks, railroad cars, or other common carriers.

(d) Universities, industries, and official agencies should cooperate in developing and implementing improved slaughtering practices and food-processing methods, with special attention to poultry and swine. The list of undesirable practices included in Chapter 8 illustrates areas where improvement is needed.

(e) More consultative and educational assistance should be provided to small industries by the states.

(f) Architectural design of processing plants should be developed to improve control of airborne contamination and cross-contamination of food and feeds during manufacture (e.g., elimination of U-shaped plant layouts).

(g) Practical quality-control guidelines should be developed for use by industry in establishing adequate quality-control practices. Such guidelines should be developed jointly by industry and regulatory agencies and should include recommendations for design and location of in-plant testing laboratories, uniform sampling procedures, and methods for testing foods and feeds.

(h) An attempt should be made to evolve a realistic assessment of the degree of hazard imposed by various foods, feeds, and drugs; and the quality-control requirements in relation to salmonella contamination should reflect the degree of hazard (see Chapter 10). Assessment of the potential hazard of a given product should reflect not only past history but also current status as determined by continuing product surveillance. Appropriate provision should be made for addition of new products to the "sensitive" group as well as for the removal of products as justified by improved industrial practices.

(i) A definite policy should be stated regarding compliance or non-compliance. The term "salmonella-free" should not be used regarding salmonellae in relation to foods because it is not possible, with certainty, to assure complete absence. Limits of acceptability can be based only on the probability that salmonellae are not present or are present at less than a statistically defined level.

Sampling procedures should be clearly described and a "cut-off" established so that industry will have a reasonable base from which to determine if its products meet requirements.

(j) Federal regulatory agencies should provide information to industry explaining and justifying proposed regulations and inspection practices. Insofar as possible effort should be made to secure compliance by distributing notices of requirements to the affected industries well in advance of any punitive action. In general, regulations should be directed toward improving a food product rather than simply toward policing it.

(k) Government, diagnostic, and industry microbiology laboratories should work together to develop a plan for reference laboratory services. Government laboratories should develop competence where it is lacking and should provide consultation and training for industry and private consulting laboratories.

(l) A model ordinance or code should be developed for the licensure or certification of independent commercial laboratories concerned with salmonellosis, and states should adopt measures to assure the competence and reliability of these laboratories.

(m) Imported foods, feeds, and drugs should meet the same standards as those imposed on domestic products.

(n) Water used for washing foods and food-plant equipment should be chlorinated or otherwise treated, if necessary, to kill salmonellae.

3. Mishandling of Food during Preparation and Serving

(a) There should be more frequent and more thorough inspections of restaurants, catering establishments, hotels, institutions, and other mass-feeding facilities. They should be made by persons who are trained in the area of food handling and facilities sanitation, and the goal should be to achieve a level of performance in food-service operations equivalent to that required of food processing. Regulations necessary to achieve salmonella control should be enacted and enforced by the appropriate local or state agency.

(b) Agreements between federal and state agencies should be devised to provide for inspection of food-service establishments that are not now adequately controlled because of confusion of responsibilities. Such facilities as restaurants on interstate highways and certain others operated on federal property are examples.

4. Education and Training

Effective control of salmonellosis depends heavily on a continuing nationwide education and training program that will inform, motivate, and periodically retrain the multitude of individuals in nearly all walks of life, who must help to improve the level of environmental sanitation and personal hygiene.

An essential aspect of the educational effort is to change the current passive attitude toward diarrheal diseases on the part of professional and nonprofessional workers, in order to get public acceptance of the inconvenience and cost associated with detection and control of salmonellosis. Active support by the medical, veterinary, and allied professions, industry and food-service management, and official federal, state, and local agencies is crucial to the success of the control of salmonellosis.

(a) The federal government should take the lead in developing a coordinated industry–professional–local–state–federal-government plan for the control of salmonellosis that will generate the technical and financial support for the expansion of education efforts on a continuing basis. To effect the plan, an official agency should be designated to coordinate operations, to develop and compile training aids, to serve as a clearinghouse for authentic information, and to evaluate and standardize training concepts. New teaching materials, such as programmed instruction courses, should be developed and used. The responsible agency should also devise mechanisms for greater sharing of information among industries and official agencies.

(b) The agency should receive assistance from an advisory committee representing appropriate professions, industries, and state and local agencies to review periodically the training materials and evaluate the effectiveness of the training effort throughout the nation.

(c) Government agencies should utilize existing private resources for training food-service personnel and should strengthen and support such resources.

(d) Federal, state, and local agencies should develop more instructional and consultative competence among their personnel. There is increasing need to emphasize the educational and consultative approach to improvement of practices and thus to reduce the need for regulatory activities. Inspectors should be well trained in methods of inspection, industry practices and problems, and legal responsibilities. Industries should participate in the training to reflect the realities of the operations under consideration.

(e) More education should be directed toward the importance of personal hygiene and food-handling practices as well as environmental sanitation. Such education should be centered at universities and schools where food-service personnel are trained. Restaurant training programs should emphasize correct personal hygiene and food-handling procedures.

(f) The teaching professions at all levels should be encouraged to incorporate sound concepts of personal hygiene and environmental sanitation in the curriculum of primary, secondary, collegiate, trade, and professional schools.

(g) More emphasis should be placed on the education of medical students and physicians in epidemiology, including that of salmonellosis, and on the physician's role in prevention and control of this disease. This training should be included in the physician's postgraduate experience as well as in his formal medical education.

(h) Hospital administrators and infections-control committees should be especially alert to the threat of salmonellosis and should give increased attention to the prevention of hospital-acquired infections. Hospital personnel should be periodically trained in good personal hygiene and good handling practices to upgrade food service and sanitation practices in the hospital, particularly in infant wards.

(i) Colleges and universities should be encouraged to educate architects and engineers in the proper design and construction of hospitals and institutions with reference to disease control, spread of infectious agents, and food-handling facilities. The same kind of education is needed with reference to proper design of food-processing plants and food-service facilities.

(j) Health-oriented professional organizations should be encouraged to organize symposia, round-table discussions, and other types of programs intended to inform their members about control of salmonellosis.

(k) Training that emphasizes the importance of personal hygiene and good sanitary and food-handling practices should be required for top management in industry so that it, in turn, can provide such training for personnel.

(l) Industry and official agencies should urge food advertisers to illustrate good sanitary practices in displays regarding foods and their preparation.

(m) Authors and publishers of cookbooks should be encouraged to include in their publications statements or rules concerning safe handling and methods of rendering food safe for use.

(n) Effective means should be devised for the education of adult audiences having diverse backgrounds and interests, including all involved professions (medical, veterinary, engineering, law, and architecture, for example), industrial workers, housewives, farmers, and others whose day-to-day cooperation is necessary for the control of salmonellosis.

(o) The public and particularly homemakers should be informed of the potential danger from turtles, baby chicks, and other pets brought into the home.

5. Research

(a) Methods should be developed for evaluating the effectiveness of salmonella control measures. For example, it is important to know the effect of eliminating salmonellae from animal feed on the incidence of salmonella infections in man and domestic animals. Similar studies should be conducted to measure the effect of eliminating certain (or all) serotypes from poultry breeder flocks on the incidence of salmonella infections in man. Development and evaluation of control measures require a baseline showing the incidence of salmonellae, but it is not feasible to obtain this information for the entire population. Therefore, studies should be conducted on a continuing basis in selected geographic areas. The results can be used to evaluate the effectiveness of control measures and, by extrapolation, to give a better idea than we now have of the magnitude of the salmonella problem.

(b) Support and encouragement should be given to development of improved equipment for food processing to replace equipment so designed that it contributes to poor sanitation in the plant.

(c) Support and encouragement should be given to research on improved laboratory methods for recovery of salmonellae from foods and for the assessment of sanitation in food-processing plants. Special attention should be given to methods that are applicable for routine process controls.

(d) Studies should be conducted to increase understanding of the nature and occurrence of salmonella infections in man and animals, the modes of transmission, the relative pathogenicity of different serotypes, including strain differences, and to define more clearly the infective dose and factors that affect host susceptibility.

(e) Research should be encouraged to explore the feasibility of immunization against salmonella infections other than typhoid fever.

(f) Studies should be conducted on ways by which raw products become contaminated and on how to protect them from contamination.

(g) Studies should be conducted to explore ways to control the presence of salmonellae in animals through improved husbandry, slaughtering, and processing practices.

(h) Studies should be conducted to define more clearly the source of salmonellae in such products as dried milk, candy, and other products not commonly regarded as sources of infection in man.

(i) Studies should be conducted to determine the influence of low levels of antibiotics in animal feed on the resistance of salmonellae to antibiotics and the effect such use of antibiotics has on salmonellosis in man.

(j) Studies should be conducted to devise techniques, comparable in effectiveness to pasteurization of milk, for destruction of salmonellae in nonfluid products. Times and temperatures required to kill some of the more common salmonellae over a wide range of water activities should be determined.

(k) Heat resistance of *Salmonella* strains in model systems should be determined over wide pH ranges and employing various organic acids to adjust the pH.

(l) Incidence in naturally contaminated foods of *Salmonella* strains that possess heat tolerance similar to serotype Senftenberg strain 775W should be determined.

(m) Research should be conducted to arrive at practical solutions to problems of motivation and conscientious use of available information. Continuing reassessment of educational efforts will be necessary, because such a program can be effective in controlling salmonellosis only when its essentials are widely and consistently practiced.

6. Other

(a) Each state should develop or have available one good salmonella typing center for reference by all laboratories in the state. Such a center should be capable of providing all industrial, private diagnostic, and public laboratories in the state with comprehensive typing service for the major serotypes. In some situations, one typing center may serve as a regional laboratory for several states. In such cases, formal contractual arrangements should be established. These centers should provide serotype information for epidemiologic studies of cases of salmonellosis and for national and state surveillance programs.

(b) Mechanisms should be developed and implemented to shorten the time between the appearance of the disease and its being reported to public health authorities.

(c) To improve salmonella surveillance within the United States, the individual states should be encouraged to develop more consistent reporting of all isolates, regardless of whether the isolation is performed in a hospital or public health or other governmental laboratory. All salmonellae isolated from man, animal, or other sources (foods or feeds, for example), whether identified as to serotype or not, should be reported to the appropriate local public health department, which should in turn routinely report to the state public health department.

(d) Increased efforts should be given to initiating investigations of salmonella episodes (selected single isolations, family outbreaks, epidemics) as soon as possible after onset. Assistance (epidemiologists, veterinarians, sanitarians, laboratory facilities and personnel, and the like) from local, state, and federal agencies needs to be publicized, and wherever not available, should be provided. The results of these investigations should be reported in detail to the appropriate local, state, and federal agencies.

7. Implementation

Salmonellosis is only one of several food-borne diseases of man, and improvement in the control of salmonellosis will result in improvement in the control of other such diseases. These recommendations *in toto* constitute an extensive and long-range approach to the control of salmonellosis in man and it is obvious that not all can be implemented immediately. Furthermore, some of them have greater potential for the reduction of salmonellosis than do others.

It is therefore suggested that the recommendations be categorized and implemented in phases. The first category, we suggest, should include those recommendations that develop mechanisms for communication, collaboration, and cooperation among the various federal and state agencies and among the official agencies and industry [for example, Recommendations 2(a), (b), (c), (e), and (k) and 3(b)].

We suggest that the second category include those recommendations that are of major communication or promotional nature, especially those dealing with agency–industry communication and education and training [for example, Recommendations 2(h) and (i) and 4(a), (b), (d), (e), and (f)].

The third category includes those recommendations that have the greatest potential for removal of salmonella from the food chain [for example, Recommendations 1(a) and 3(a)].

During the first year of implementation, the first category [except Recommendation 2(c)] and Recommendations 2(h) and (i) of the second category should be completed, and Recommendations 4(a), (b), (d), (e), and (f) of the second category should be initiated.

During the second year, the recommendations of the third category should be initiated.

The remaining recommendations should be given priority ratings, placing emphasis on the promotional and educational recommendations, and implemented as quickly as feasible. Within five years, discernible progress on all recommendations should be evident if timely control of salmonellosis is to be achieved.

II
THE DISEASE

4 Seriousness of the Problem

Salmonellosis is one of the most significant communicable diseases in the United States. Human morbidity in the United States due to salmonella infection is conservatively estimated at 2,000,000 cases per year; although, as with all food-borne disease, the true magnitude of the problem is not known. The incidence of clinical salmonellosis is highest at the age extremes, that is, among the very young and the elderly. However, all age groups are susceptible. Mortality, though less than one percent of those with clinical disease, most often involves persons with underlying major disease problems. The interrelationships between man and animals makes salmonellosis a more difficult problem than most other communicable diseases.

The Salmonella Surveillance Program, which was initiated at the National Communicable Disease Center in 1963 in cooperation with the State and Territorial Epidemiologists and Laboratory Directors, is based on weekly reports from each state listing the serotypes that have been identified in the state laboratory. Additionally, weekly reports are received from the District of Columbia; the Salmonella Reference Center–Beth Israel Hospital, New York City; The New York City Public Health Department; the U.S. Department of Agriculture; the National Animal Disease Laboratory, Ames, Iowa; and the U.S. Food and Drug Administration. The instances reported represent individual isolations from a single episode of infection, whether a clinical case or a carrier; repeat isolations from the same individual are not included. Interpretations are limited by the bias inherent in the data analyzed. For example, geographical prevalence and age of patients may reflect "interest factors."

29

Additionally, such factors as seriousness of disease and a lack of adequate laboratory facilities in some areas influence the results presented.

In Figure 2, a comparison of the reported incidence of salmonellosis in the United States with typhoid fever from 1942 to 1967 is presented. As can be seen, the reported incidence of salmonellosis (other than typhoid fever) increased strikingly between 1942 and 1963. The increased number of cases reported were in part due to general improvements in medical care, greater availability of laboratory facilities, better techniques of isolation and identification, improved reporting of salmo-

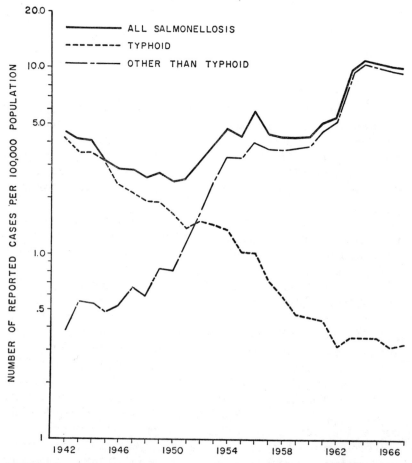

FIGURE 2   Reported incidence of human salmonellosis in the United States, 1942–1967. From National Communicable Disease Center, Salmonella Surveillance Report, Annual Summary 1967.

nellosis, increasing number of investigations, and improvement in communications between states and the Public Health Service. Since 1964, however, the reported incidence has been essentially constant (Figure 3). During 1967, 19,723 isolations of salmonellae from human subjects were reported.[1]

Even though these data show a leveling of reported isolations during the past several years, there are some significant factors, suggesting that the true incidence, as well as the opportunity for interstate epidemics, may have increased during the past 20 years. These include: (1) a change in eating habits from home-prepared to communal meals in schools, in restaurants, and other mass-feeding establishments; (2) the widespread consumption of raw or slightly heated products of animal origin; (3) the mass production of processed foods, such as cake mixes, and their subsequent countrywide distribution and use[2]; (4) the increasing consumption of poultry and poultry products during the past 15 years; (5) the increasing number of foods and other products found contaminated with salmonella (to the foodstuffs previously recognized as being associated with salmonellosis must be added dried milk, smoked fish, yeast, and carmine dye; pharmaceutical products of animal origin, such as pancreatin, pepsin, bile salts, gelatin, and vitamins, and extracts of thyroid, adrenal cortex, pancreas, pituitary, liver, and stomach may also be contaminated); (6) the increasing association of salmonellosis with such pets as turtles and chicks; (7) application of food hygiene measures that may eliminate bacterial flora that otherwise might either inhibit the growth of salmonella or spoil the food in question so that consumers would discard it without use[3]; (8) evidence that suggests

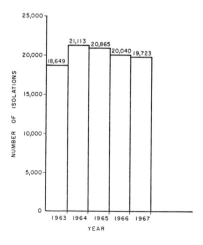

FIGURE 3   Reported human isolations of salmonellae in the United States, 1963–1967. From National Communicable Disease Center, Salmonella Surveillance Report, Annual Summary 1967.

that the increasing use of antibiotics in man, whether for treatment of clinical salmonellosis or not, contributes to the prolongation of the salmonella carrier state (the carrier rate is not accurately known, but has been estimated at from 2 to 50 per thousand in the normal population).

As stated, conservative estimates suggest that the true number of cases of salmonellosis in the United States is closer to 2,000,000 than to the reported 20,000 each year. There is ample evidence to support the conclusion that salmonellosis is grossly underreported. For example, during the water-borne outbreak of gastroenteritis caused by serotype Typhimurium in Riverside, California, in 1965, there were 110 human isolations, and approximately 200 cases of gastroenteritis were known to the health department; but the epidemiologic evidence indicated that there were at least 16,000 cases of gastroenteritis. Another example is that of Oxford, Nebraska, where in 1967 there was an outbreak of Typhimurium gastroenteritis following the consumption of contaminated turkeys. There were five isolations from individuals with clinical disease reported through normal reporting channels; however, during a stool culture survey, 261 isolations were made, 158 from individuals with clinical disease and 103 from asymptomatic carriers. In fact, however, an estimated 2,600 infections occurred as determined by epidemiologic investigations, resulting in 1,900 clinically ill individuals and 700 asymptomatic carriers.

During the serious interstate outbreak of gastroenteritis (originating from eggs contaminated with serotype Derby) in 1963 that involved 53 hospitals in 13 states, there would have been fewer than 100 cases reported through the normal channels. However, as a result of special studies initiated in involved hospitals, over 1,000 cases were identified by bacterial culture of stool specimens.

Taking salmonellae isolations as a whole, approximately 55 percent represent the sporadic incident or case; 20 percent, a family incident or outbreak (two or more isolations of the same serotype from the same family); 15 percent, a general incident or outbreak; and 10 percent, hospital-associated infections. There is evidence to suggest that when a single isolation is reported, there are one or more additional associated cases within the family that, being uncultured, go unreported. With improved surveillance, investigation, and reporting, the number of single isolations significantly increases. This concept is exemplified by investigations conducted in 1962, in the Midwest, in which attempts were made to study single isolations of serotype Hartford, at that time a rarely isolated serotype. In each instance in which a family isolation of serotype Hartford was reported, additional cases of gastroenteritis were uncovered; and not infrequently rectal swabs, obtained at the time of the visit, from family members other than the index case were positive for serotype Hartford.

The seasonal distribution of salmonellae isolations from man, from 1963 through 1967, is shown in Figure 4. A consistent seasonal pattern is apparent, the greatest number of isolations being reported from July through October for each year and the lowest number from January to May.

A reported 155 different serotypes of *Salmonella* were isolated from man in 1967[1] (Table 1). Thus only about 12 percent of the more than 1,300 known serotypes were involved.

The ten most frequently reported serotypes are listed in Table 2. These ten serotypes accounted for 14,001 (71.0 percent) of the 19,723 isolates reported during 1967. As in previous years, serotypes Typhimurium and serotype Typhimurium var. copenhagen together were the most frequently reported serotypes during 1967, comprising 29.4 percent of all isolations, and were also the most frequently reported serotypes for each month of 1967. Serotype Heidelberg, the second most frequently reported serotype, accounted for 8.4 percent of the total isolations.

Table 2 demonstrates the close correlation between human and non-human sources of salmonellae, with four serotypes appearing on both lists. The similarities confirm the importance of the nonhuman reservoirs of salmonellae in the epidemiology of human salmonellosis.

The geographic distribution of salmonella isolations reported during 1967 appears in Figure 5. California reported the largest number, 2,128; other states reporting over 1,000 isolates were New York, Massachusetts,

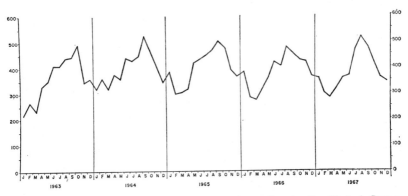

FIGURE 4   Reported human isolations of salmonellae in the United States, 1963–1967. From National Communicable Disease Center, Salmonella Surveillance Report, Annual Summary 1967.

TABLE 2   Ten Most Common Serotypes Isolated in the United States in 1967[a]

Serotype	Human Rank	Number	Percent	Nonhuman Rank	Number	Percent
Typhimurium and Typhimurium var. copenhagen	1	5,803	29.4	1	1,146	13.0
Heidelberg	2	1,648	8.4	2	665	7.6
Enteritidis	3	1,277	6.5			
Newport	4	1,263	6.4			
Infantis	5	980	5.0	5	424	4.3
Saint-paul	6	907	4.6	6	381	4.3
S. typhi	7	690	3.5			
Blockley	8	519	2.6			
Thompson	9	508	2.6			
Oranienburg	10	406	2.1			
Anatum				3	521	5.9
Derby				4	458	5.2
Montevideo				7	335	3.8
Tennessee				8	322	3.7
Eimbuettel				9	308	3.5
Senftenberg				10	274	3.1
Subtotal		14,001	71.0		4,834	55.0
Total all serotypes		19,723			8,794	

[a] From National Communicable Disease Center, Salmonella Surveillance Report, Annual Summary 1967.

Illinois, Florida, and Texas. These geographic data are influenced by local interest factors, availability of physicians, and laboratories.

The reported incidence of salmonella infection for the entire country was 10.0 per 100,000. Hawaii, as in past years, reported the highest incidence, 85.9 per 100,000. Other areas reporting incidence rates higher than 20 per 100,000 were New Mexico, Massachusetts, Louisiana, Florida, and the District of Columbia.

The importance of specific serotypes varied geographically (Table 1). As had been observed in previous years, several serotypes occurred in definite regional patterns. For example, Hawaii, which accounted for only 3.2 percent of national salmonella isolations, reported 97 percent (59 of 61) of all isolations of serotype Oslo, and 44 percent (24 of 55) of isolations of serotype Livingstone. Other regional patterns appeared. Serotype Javiana was isolated almost exclusively in the central and south-

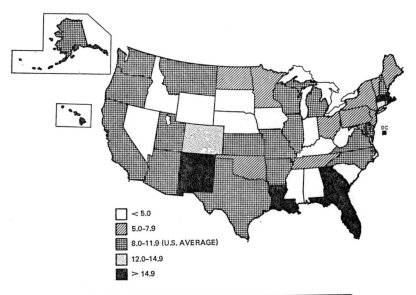

☐	< 5.0
▨	5.0–7.9
▦	8.0–11.9 (U.S. AVERAGE)
▨	12.0–14.9
■	> 14.9

State	Number of Isolations	Rate Per 100,000		State	Number of Isolations	Rate Per 100,000	
Alabama	130	3.7	(+)	Montana	58	8.3	(–)
Alaska	22	8.1	(–)	Nebraska	24	1.7	(+)
Arizona	148	9.1	(–)	Nevada	19	4.3	(+)
Arkansas	221	11.2	(–)	New Hampshire	60	8.7	(–)
California	2,128	11.1	(+)	New Jersey	444	6.3	(–)
Colorado	267	13.5	(–)	New Mexico	324	32.3	(+)
Connecticut	354	12.1	(+)	New York	1,417	7.7	(–)
Delaware	55	10.5	(–)	North Carolina	488	9.7	(+)
Dist. of Col.	166	20.5	(–)	North Dakota	36	5.6	(+)
Florida	1,227	20.5	(+)	Ohio	601	5.7	(+)
Georgia	690	15.3	(+)	Oklahoma	179	7.2	(+)
Hawaii	635	85.9	(+)	Oregon	188	9.4	(–)
Idaho	29	4.1	(–)	Pennsylvania	907	7.8	(+)
Illinois	1,259	11.6	(+)	Rhode Island	72	8.0	(+)
Indiana	206	4.1	(–)	South Carolina	7	0.3	(–)
Iowa	113	4.1	(–)	South Dakota	20	3.0	(+)
Kansas	261	11.5	(–)	Tennessee	234	6.0	(–)
Kentucky	78	2.4	(–)	Texas	1,133	10.4	(+)
Louisiana	758	20.7	(–)	Utah	121	11.8	(–)
Maine	68	7.0	(–)	Vermont	23	5.5	(+)
Maryland	405	11.0	(–)	Virginia	391	8.6	(+)
Massachusetts	1,302	24.0	(–)	Washington	368	11.9	(–)
Michigan	699	8.1	(–)	West Virginia	44	2.4	(+)
Minnesota	263	7.3	(–)	Wisconsin	440	10.5	(–)
Mississippi	87	3.7	(+)	Wyoming	6	1.9	(+)
Missouri	548	11.9	(+)	TOTALS	19,723	10.0	(–2.0%)

(+) Increase over 1966   (–) Decrease from 1966

FIGURE 5   Number of human isolations of salmonella per 100,000 population in the United States in 1967. From U.S. Department of Commerce, Current Population Reports, Series P-25, No. 380.

ern states; and two states, Texas and Florida, accounted for 61 percent of the 373 isolations of this serotype. Nine of 11 isolations of serotype Saphra were from Texas, continuing a trend first noted in 1965; 75 percent of isolations of serotype Miami (52 of 69) were from Florida; and all the isolations of serotype Atlanta (11 of 11) were from Georgia.

Of the 19,067 individuals (of the total 19,723 cases of salmonellosis reported) for whom sex was reported during 1967, 9,490 (49.8 percent) were males, and 9,577 (50.2 percent) were females (Table 3). Although there appears to be no sex predilection, it is interesting that there is a significant preponderance of males in the age group under 20 years and a preponderance of females in the age group over 20 years. A similar distribution has been seen for the past four years. The age–sex distribution for 1967 is (unknown and unspecified ages not included):

Age (years)	Male		Female		Total
	Number	Percent	Number	Percent	
Less than 20	4,877	53.5	4,238	46.5	9,115
20 and over	1,911	41.9	2,646	58.1	4,557
TOTAL	6,788	49.6	6,884	50.4	13,672

Of the 13,672 individuals reported by age during 1967, 9,115 (66.7 percent) were less than 20 years of age.

TABLE 3   Age and Sex Distribution of 19,723 Individuals Reported as Harboring Salmonellae during 1967[a]

Age (years)	Male	Female	Unknown	Total	Percent	Cumulative Percent
Under 1	1,342	1,224	32	2,598	18.9	18.9
1–4	1,922	1,555	16	3,493	25.4	44.3
5–9	870	717	4	1,591	11.6	55.9
10–19	743	742	4	1,489	10.8	66.7
20–29	525	711	2	1,238	9.0	75.7
30–39	329	486	4	819	6.0	81.7
40–49	289	437	4	730	5.3	87.0
50–59	301	356	2	659	4.8	91.8
60–69	266	303	0	569	4.1	95.9
70–79	126	237	2	365	2.7	98.6
80+		116	1	192	1.4	100.0
SUBTOTAL	6,788	6,884	71	13,743		
Child (unspec.)	86	84	19	189		
Adult (unspec.)	86	141	5	232		
Unknown	2,530	2,468	561	5,559		
TOTAL	9,490	9,577	656	19,723		
PERCENT	49.8	50.2				

[a] From National Communicable Disease Center, Salmonella Surveillance Report, Annual Summary 1967.

Figure 6 demonstrates the number of isolations per 100,000 in various age groups for 1967. This pattern closely approximates those for the years 1963 through 1966. However, the rates in the age groups less than 10 appears to have been increasing over the past five years. This is particularly true in the less-than-one-year age group, where the rates per 100,000 have been 44, 53, 63, 69, and 74, respectively, for the years 1963 through 1967. In figure 6, isolations in this age group are further divided by age in months. The rate of isolations rises to an incidence greater than 100 isolations per 100,000 population between 2 and 4 months of age and gradually declines to an incidence of 30 per 100,000 at 11 months.

Of 18,852 isolations of 151 different salmonella serotypes in 1967 (excluding *Salmonella typhi* and serotypes Paratyphi A, B, and C), 2,677 (14.2 percent), representing 85 different serotypes, were isolated from nonfecal sources, including 344 from blood (12.8 percent), 248 from urine (9.3 percent), and 2,085 (77.9 percent) from other sources (gallbladder, spinal fluid, sputum, etc.). Nonfecal isolations of the ten most common serotypes are presented in Table 4. Typhimurium was the serotype most commonly isolated from nonfecal sources, with 700 non-

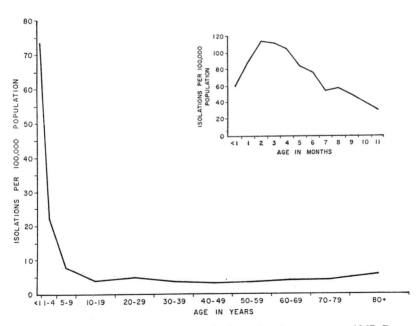

FIGURE 6   Rate of human isolations of salmonellae by age group, 1967. Population data derived from U.S. Department of Commerce, Current Population Reports, Series P-25, No. 385.

fecal isolations out of 5,530 isolations from all sources (12.7 percent). However, for several serotypes the proportion of all isolations that were nonfecal exceeded that of Typhimurium: serotype Heidelberg (20.9 percent), serotype Enteritidis (19.5 percent), and serotype Oranienburg (16.7 percent). It is of interest that 24 of 27 isolations of *Salmonella cholerae-suis* and *S. cholerae-suis* var. *kunzendorf* (88.9 percent) were from nonfecal sources. Seventy serotypes, representing 263 isolates, were reported from stool cultures only.

TABLE 4   Nonfecal Isolations of the Ten Most Common Salmonella Serotypes Isolated from Man, 1967

Serotype	Blood	Urine	Other	Total Nonfecal Isolations	Total Isolations All Sources	Percent Nonfecal Isolations
Typhimurium	114	47	539	700	5,530	12.7
Heidelberg	45	28	272	345	1,648	20.9
Enteritidis	59	22	168	249	1,277	19.5
Newport	8	13	108	129	1,263	10.2
Infantis	11	12	76	99	980	10.1
Saint-paul	12	16	87	115	907	12.7
Blockley	2	5	54	61	519	11.8
Thompson	5	9	39	53	508	10.4
Oranienburg	10	6	52	68	406	16.7
Montevideo	8	5	35	48	398	12.1
SUBTOTAL	274	163	1,430	1,867	13,436	13.9
TOTAL (all serotypes)[a]	344	248	2,085	2,677	18,852	14.2

[a] Excluding *Salmonella typhi* and serotypes Paratyphi A, B, and C.

The age distribution of persons from whom nonfecal isolations were made is presented in Table 5. Of 13,743 isolates reported by source and age, 1,766 (12.8 percent) were from nonfecal sources. Nonfecal isolations were more frequent in the older age groups, comprising 11.7 percent of isolations from persons less than 50 compared with 20.5 percent of isolations from persons of over 50. The difference is statistically significant ($p < 0.0005$). Separate analyses of age distribution for isolations from blood and urine demonstrated a similar preponderance in the elderly.

It is not possible to assess accurately the number of deaths related to salmonella infection. Reporting officials are not always provided information concerning the clinical status of the individual from whom an isolation has been made. Also, since fatal cases of salmonellosis often

TABLE 5   Age Distribution of Persons with Nonfecal Isolations of Salmonellae, 1967

Age (years)	No. Nonfecal Isolations	Total Isolations All sources	Total in Percent
<10	811	7,682	10.6
10–19	235	1,489	15.8
20–29	162	1,238	13.1
30–39	98	819	12.0
40–49	94	730	12.9
50–59	109	659	16.5
60–69	122	569	21.4
70–79	97	365	26.6
>79	38	192	19.8
TOTAL	1,766	13,743	12.8

occur in patients with severe underlying illness, it can be difficult to assess the role of the salmonella infection in the final outcome. Finally, cases in which isolates are reported prior to death would not be reported as fatalities.

The best measurement of mortality available is the case–fatality ratio of clinical salmonellosis that is obtained by studying investigated outbreaks. In the 29 outbreaks reported in the Salmonella Surveillance Reports in 1967, 13 deaths occurred among 5,761 cases, representing a death-to-case ratio of 0.22 percent. Almost all of these fatalities occurred in young infants, the elderly, and persons severely ill with other diseases.

The hospitalized patient presents a special problem in that many of the epidemics reported have involved institutionalized people and have been persistent. The hospitalized patient faces greater risk than does the general population because he is generally older or very young and frequently has concurrent chronic or acute disease, and his resistance to infection is not uncommonly reduced because of various diagnostic and therapeutic maneuvers. Some hospitalized patients, such as those with gastrointestinal-tract diseases, are under special risk either because of their underlying disease or because they are receiving food items frequently associated with salmonellosis, e.g., raw eggnog or protein supplements. Chronic-care and mental institutions encounter situations similar to those of the acute-care facilities. Finally, nursery outbreaks, often resulting from person-to-person transmission, have proved to be serious.

The problem of salmonellosis among patients in patient-care institutions is compounded when service personnel having varying degrees of contact with patients become contaminated with salmonella organisms, but do not themselves develop clinical disease. Unless special efforts are made to identify these carriers, the salmonella problem can rebound between patients and personnel, personnel and personnel, personnel and patients, for prolonged periods, as was exemplified in some of the institutions involved in the serotype Derby outbreak in 1963.

Thus the institutional problem in facilities for both acute and chronic patient care occasions special concern. During the five-year period 1963–1967, the Salmonella Surveillance Program of the National Communicable Disease Center recorded 40 epidemics of salmonellosis in hospitals and institutions involving 3,025 patients, among whom there were 43 deaths. Epidemics occurred in nurseries for newborns, pediatric wards, general hospital wards, nursing homes, and mental institutions. These outbreaks emphasize the need for institutions to develop effective surveillance programs that are sensitive enough to record the sporadic case of salmonellosis that occurs among patients or personnel, as well as the cases associated with an outbreak. To be effective, a surveillance program must be coordinated with the activities of an infections-control committee and under the direction of the hospital epidemiologist or a consultant functioning as the epidemiologist.

In addition to preventing the spread of salmonellae from carriers or cases among patients and personnel, the institution must be sure that its standard of food service is maintained at a level that prevents introduction of salmonellae in this way. Institutional purchasing agents must be alert so that foods contaminated with salmonellae are not brought into the institution even if they are to be further processed.

In 1967, 29 outbreaks involving 12,961 individuals were reported in the Salmonella Surveillance Reports. Of 25 food-borne outbreaks, 18 were traced to a specific contaminated food, including 7 caused by contaminated eggs, 5 by contaminated turkey, 2 by pork, 2 by beef, 1 by raw milk, and 1 by potato salad; in 7 food-borne outbreaks, the specific food could not be identified. Vehicles involved demonstrate the significance of animal reservoirs in the transmission of salmonellosis and provide direction to necessary control measures.

Six outbreaks, involving 187 persons, occurred in hospitals and were responsible for 10 of the 13 deaths related to outbreaks. Although these outbreaks accounted for only 21 percent of reported outbreaks, they accounted for 77 percent of all fatalities.

Although the etiology of all outbreaks was confirmed bacteriologically, many of the 12,965 ill individuals were never cultured and are not included as reported isolations in the national surveillance data. In the two largest outbreaks reported in 1967, involving a total of 10,900 persons, only about 1 percent of those ill were cultured and reported. Only a small part of the total of 19,723 isolations of salmonellae in 1967 were from reported outbreaks, suggesting that these outbreaks represent only a small fraction of the outbreaks actually occurring in the United States.

ECONOMIC IMPORTANCE

Human salmonellosis can cause significant economic losses as the result of direct medical payments and lost working days. In Riverside, California, there were 70 people hospitalized because of serotype Typhimurium gastroenteritis, and in Oxford, Nebraska, there were 12 people hospitalized. During an interstate outbreak of salmonellosis, in which the vehicle of infection was a frozen dessert, there were an estimated 1,790 people ill, the majority of whom missed from 2 to 7 days of work or school, and 2 percent of whom were hospitalized. In an outbreak of serotype Infantis gastroenteritis attributed to consumption of smoked ham, probably contaminated in the kitchen, 37 of 55 individuals who consumed the vehicle became ill. Ten were hospitalized, with an average hospitalization of 5.5 days.

Accurate information concerning economic losses is not readily available, but some studies have been made. In an outbreak of serotype Typhimurium gastroenteritis in Wichita, Kansas, in which 700 of 1,300 individuals who attended a banquet became ill, it is estimated that 450 persons sought medical attention at an average cost close to $45.00 per person. The total medical care cost was estimated at $20,250. The 700 people lost an average of 2.9 working days each for an economic loss of approximately $28,000. Thus, the total financial losses to those attending the banquet were $48,000. It is estimated that the direct financial losses of the people in Riverside, California, amounted to $75,000. During the outbreak of serotype Derby gastroenteritis described earlier, the increased patient costs amounted to at least $125,000, and the costs to hospitals from which these data were made available were at least $90,000. These cost estimates do not include the salaries lost to the patient because of absenteeism from work or to a parent who has to stay at home to take care of an ill child.

If we assume that there are approximately 2,000,000 cases of salmonella gastroenteritis among humans in the United States annually, the total economic impact due to patients' disabilities could be estimated at from $20 million to $200 million. There are also the costs associated with preventive measures, such as routine stool cultures from food handlers and environmental and product cultures in manufacturing companies, and the great expense associated with recall of commercial items found to be contaminated with salmonella. For example, in 1967, the cost of recalling chocolate candy following detection of salmonellae has been estimated at $5 million. An earlier recall of a dried milk preparation probably cost at least as much.

NONHUMAN SALMONELLOSIS

It has been estimated that from 1 to 3 percent of all domestic animals are infected with salmonellae. However, culture surveys among a variety of animals reveal recovery rates ranging up to 50 percent, depending on the species and other variables. Not only might infection with salmonellae cause morbidity and mortality among the animals, but considering that many of the chains of infection include both animals and man, it is evident that salmonellosis among animals will have an effect on man. Some current methods of animal production are associated with an increased possibility of salmonellosis. For example, mass production involving calves, beef cattle, swine, and poultry confined to relatively small areas increases the potential spread of salmonellosis among these animals. The problems with poultry and swine are also directly related to the use of contaminated feed. Due to the increasing demand for poultry, there are larger breeding flocks and greater concentration of birds during transportation, slaughter, and processing, all of which aid the transmission of salmonella among the birds. For all animals, the possible relation of antibiotics in feed to the development of resistant organisms and the emergence of Resistance Transfer Factor should be assessed.

During 1967, 8,794 salmonella isolations from nonhuman sources were reported (Figure 7). The number of nonhuman isolations has increased each year since 1963, but this probably reflects increasing surveillance. The sources of these isolations are shown in Figure 8. The number and percent of isolations by source demonstrate the importance of poultry and poultry products as vehicles for salmonellosis. Turkey, chicken, eggs, and egg products, which together were responsible for 48 percent of the food-borne outbreaks reported in 1967, accounted for 33.8 percent of all nonhuman isolations. Swine and cattle accounted for 16.2 percent of all nonhuman recoveries, and dried milk and other human foods for 13.4 percent. Isolations from animal feedstuffs accounted for 17.5 percent during 1967. This represents a slight increase over 1966 and an almost threefold increase over previous years and reflects continued and increased interest in the surveillance of animal feeds.

The ten most common salmonella serotypes isolated from nonhuman

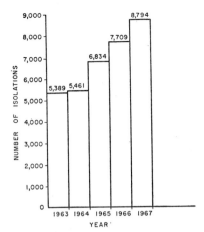

FIGURE 7   Reported nonhuman isolations of salmonellae in the United States, 1963–1967. From National Communicable Disease Center, Salmonella Surveillance Report, Annual Summary 1967.

sources during 1967 are listed in Table 2. These ten serotypes comprised 55 percent of all nonhuman isolates. It is difficult to assign relative importance to the various nonhuman isolations, because much of the sampling done represents interest factors, such as special studies and economic importance.

The economic losses associated with animal salmonellosis can only be roughly estimated. During fiscal year 1964–1965, 37 million fowl were tested under the national program for the control of serotypes Pullorum, Gallinarum, and Typhimurium. Based on a cost of about 10¢ per test, the estimated cost to the national industry was approximately $4 million for blood testing alone. If a greater amount of salmonellosis is assumed in the total population and assuming a loss based on ¼ ¢ per bird for the approximate 2.6 billion birds produced in the United States last year, there would be another $6.5 million lost to industry. These calculations are confirmed by data presented at the National Conference on Salmonellosis, March 1964, at which Dr. John W. Walker of the USDA reported "the present pullorum/typhoid control program costs participants in the National Poultry Improvement Plans $10,000,000 a year." The success of the pullorum control program has made it economically practical to expand poultry production from a household enterprise to a $10 billion industry. Any relaxation of control would very likely result in serious difficulties for the industry. The USDA has furnished data to this Committee indicating that the economic importance of salmonella infection in the livestock and poultry industries is the sum of:

- Mortality and morbidity losses of infected animals (including dairy calves)
- Cost of veterinary services and drugs

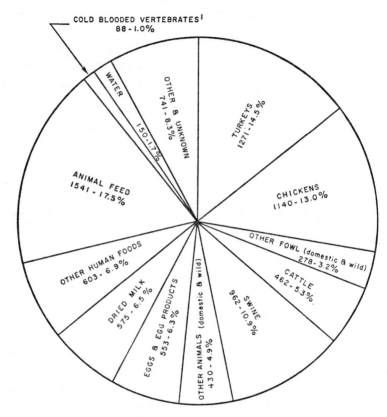

COLD BLOODED VERTEBRATES[1]
88 - 1.0%

WATER
150 - 1.7%

OTHER & UNKNOWN
741 - 8.3%

ANIMAL FEED
1541 - 17.5%

TURKEYS
1271 - 14.5%

CHICKENS
1140 - 13.0%

OTHER FOWL (domestic & wild)
278 - 3.2%

CATTLE
462 - 5.3%

SWINE
962 - 10.9%

OTHER ANIMALS (domestic & wild)
430 - 4.9%

EGGS & EGG PRODUCTS
553 - 6.3%

DRIED MILK
575 - 6.5%

OTHER HUMAN FOODS
603 - 6.9%

[1]INCLUDES 57 TURTLE ISOLATES

FIGURE 8   Number and percentage of nonhuman salmonellae isolations from the indicated sources in the United States in 1967. From National Communicable Disease Center, Salmonella Surveillance Report, Annual Summary 1967.

- Decreased milk production in dairy cattle
- Decreased rate of weight gain for beef cattle, swine, lambs, broilers, and turkeys
- Decreased egg production
- Loss of consumer confidence in dairy and poultry products, especially eggs, reflected in decreased price at the producer level
- Cost to the processor for recalling, reprocessing, and/or destroying livestock, dairy, and poultry products found to be contaminated with salmonella after processing and/or distribution in channels of trade

Some estimates of the economic importance of salmonellosis to the individual farmer can be obtained from the data in *Requests for Salmonella Serotyping Reports,* submitted to the Animal Health Division by local livestock diagnostic laboratories. Reporting procedures initiated in 1966 permit some estimation of the percentage of mortality on a herd basis associated with each culture submitted for serotyping. The average reported mortality in 1966 per herd or flock for all serotypes by species is as follows: cattle, 1.84 percent; swine, 3.03 percent; chickens, 1.02 percent; turkeys, 2.26 percent. These figures represent minimum losses, based on the number of deaths that had occurred at the time the specimens were collected for laboratory examination. There is no report or investigation of subsequent mortality in these herds.

A particularly important problem is salmonellosis in calves. A report from Michigan states that on 26 farms during a 20-month period, there was mortality of 23.6 percent due to salmonellosis (155 calves of a total of 663).[4] Poor housing arrangements and sanitation, acquisition of calves from other herds, and premature weaning were considered to be important contributing factors.

Available reports on production losses are limited to individual case reports. For example, in a reported outbreak of serotype Typhimurium in a 52-cow dairy herd, milk production dropped 10 cans (approximately 90 gallons, 774 pounds) overnight. Assuming that this was an average herd in the state concerned (annual production of 9,800 pounds per cow), this one-day loss of 774 pounds (55 percent) from an estimated daily production of about 1,396 pounds represents a loss to the farmer of $37.15 from milk production alone. In 72 hours, most of the cattle had responded favorably to treatment. However, it was two weeks before normal milk production was restored.

Reduced consumer demand for livestock and poultry products as a result of reports of salmonella contamination is reflected in a decreased price at the producer level. This price decrease is difficult to estimate because of the normal fluctuation in prices farmers receive for their product. The impact of the serotype Derby outbreak in Philadelphia and New York in 1963 resulted in an estimated reduction of 1¢ per dozen in the price farmers received for their eggs in East Coast markets. This reduction lasted for a period of four to six months. Based on an average production of 20 dozen eggs per bird per year, this represents a loss to the producer of $100 per 1,000 laying birds.

REFERENCES

1. Salmonella Surveillance—Annual Summary, National Communicable Disease Center, Atlanta, Georgia (1967).

2. Food Protection Committee, Food and Nutrition Board, *An Evaluation of Public Health Hazards from Microbiological Contamination of Foods,* NAS-NRC Publ. 1195, Natl. Acad. Sci.–Natl. Res. Council, Washington, D.C. (1964).
3. Joint FAO/WHO Expert Committee on Zoonoses—Third Report—WHO Tech. Rep. Ser. No. 378 (1967), page 34.
4. H. Rothenbacker, "Mortality and Morbidity in Calves with Salmonellosis," *J. Amer. Vet. Med. Ass.,* 147, 1211 (1965).
5. S. A. Schroeder, B. Aserkoff, and P. S. Brachman, "Epidemic Salmonellosis in Hospitals and Institutions," *N. Engl. J. Med.,* 279, 674 (1968).

5 The Causal Organism

The genus *Salmonella** is within the family Enterobacteriaceae and is defined[1,2] as follows:

> The genus *Salmonella* is composed of motile bacteria that conform to the definitions of the family ENTEROBACTERIACEAE and the tribe SALMONELLEAE. Urease is not produced, sodium malonate is not utilized, gelatin is not liquefied, and growth does not occur in medium containing potassium cyanide. Lysine, arginine, and ornithine are decarboxylated. Acid is produced in Jordan's tartrate medium. Dulcitol is fermented and inositol is utilized by numerous strains. Sucrose, salicin, raffinose, and lactose are not fermented.

Occasionally an aberrant strain of one of the commonly occurring salmonellae may be seen. Such a culture may ferment lactose, sucrose, or salicin, or it may form indol. These are exceptional,[1,3,4] and if all the other biochemical reactions are like those given by salmonellae, then these aberrant strains are members of the genus *Salmonella*. In other words, the determination as to whether a microorganism is a member of the genus is made on the basis of all its biochemical characteristics, not by means of a single test such as lactose utilization or lack of it. A strain that ferments lactose, for example, may occur in a product[5] and give rise to a number of infections, but it should

---

* The generic term *Salmonella* was given to these microorganisms by Lignières in 1900[7,11] in honor of Dr. D. E. Salmon, a codiscoverer of the microorganism now known as *Salmonella cholerae-suis*. This generic term was adopted by international agreement on the basis of priority, in accordance with international rules of nomenclature, and has been employed universally since 1933.

47

be recalled that it is still a single strain represented by multiple isolants. Or, to put it another way, the aberrant strain represents one focus of infection with multiple cases (and isolates). This fact should be taken into account in attempts to determine the frequency of occurrence of aberrant strains of salmonellae. Further, it should be recalled that with very few exceptions,[1, 4] strains seen in daily practice are perfectly typical, a fact that is more remarkable perhaps than the occurrence of an occasional aberrant culture. Nevertheless, aberrant strains should be recognized when they occur, and it is for this reason that the use of bismuth sulfite agar, along with other plating media, is recommended[6] for the isolation of salmonellae.

The nomenclature system adopted for use here is that proposed in 1963[7] (with emendations[2, 8]). This system and the definitions were adopted by the Subcommittee on Enterobacteriaceae of the American Society for Microbiology.[9, 10] The subject of speciation within the genus *Salmonella* has been discussed elsewhere.[1, 7] Suffice it to say that the "three species concept" of speciation was adopted[7] as the simplest and most logical of several alternatives. The species of *Salmonella* recognized are: *Salmonella cholerae-suis,* the type species according to the Salmonella Committee,[11] *Salmonella typhi,* and *Salmonella enteritidis.** *S. enteritidis* was selected as the name for the third species because it was the oldest validly published name other than that of the type species and *S. typhi.* All salmonellae other than *S. cholerae-suis* and *S. typhi* are considered to be serotypes of *S. enteritidis,* e.g., *S. enteritidis* serotype Enteritidis and *S. enteritidis* serotype Typhimurium. The names applied to serotypes of *Salmonella* in the *Salmonella* Schema are used in lieu of expressing the antigenic formulas. Such serotypic names are infrasubspecific designations and as such have no standing in nomenclature. The designations for the numerous serotypes of *S. enteritidis* are capitalized simply to make them more easily recognizable. After a microorganism has been identified as a member of the genus *Salmonella* by biochemical tests, it is characterized further by determination of its antigenic structure by serologic methods.[3, 12] First the somatic (O) antigen group of a culture is determined (O groupings), then the flagellar (H) antigens are studied. The majority of salmonellae are diphasic, i.e., their flagellar antigens are of two kinds, called phases, which are reversible. When the antigenic formula (O and H antigens) of a culture have been characterized, its serotypic name is determined by consulting an antigenic schema.[3, 12] The antigenic formulas of the 50 (or 57†) commonly oc-

---

* Not to be confused with serotype Enteritidis.

† The larger number depends upon whether biotypes and other variants are counted separately.

curring serotypes of *Salmonella* are given in a table in Appendix A. Parenthetically, the antisera, including absorbed single factor O and H antisera, that are required for complete serologic typing of the species and serotypes listed in the above-mentioned table (Appendix A) rapidly are becoming available from commercial sources. Clearly many additional serotypes can be completely or partially characterized with these same antisera.

Members of the genus *Salmonella* are widely distributed in nature, and they may be the primary etiological agents of disease or may superimpose themselves, as secondary invaders, upon a pre-existing infection caused by another agent. When placed in a suitable environment inside or outside the body of an animal (including man) salmonellae will multiply. Although there are some exceptions, the natural reservoir of these microorganisms is the animal kingdom in general. Salmonellae are not indigenous either to normal or diseased plants or plant tissues. However, the natural or essential ecology of salmonellae frequently is disturbed by man, and this results in incidental distribution of the bacteria to sites not a part of their essential ecology. Salmonellae are not known to be indigenous to such foodstuffs as fish, shellfish, or watermelon, but these foodstuffs have been implicated in outbreaks of salmonellosis (see Chapter 6).

A study of how man becomes infected is in fact a study of the ecology, epidemiology, and epizootiology of salmonellae.

ECOLOGICAL DIVISIONS OF *SALMONELLA*

There are three divisions into which members of the genus may be placed according to their host preferences or adaptions.

1. Those more or less strictly adapted to man, such as *Salmonella typhi* and *Salmonella enteritidis* serotypes Paratyphi A, Paratyphi C, and Sendai. These salmonellae have no known secondary hosts, hence they are found very rarely in other animals (very occasional accidental infections). The characteristics of these salmonellae are:

- Small dosage required to produce disease
- Prolonged incubation period (10 to 20 or more days)
- Enteric fever produced (bloodstream invasion) as opposed to acute gastroenteritis*
- Tendency to produce permanent carriers and to become endemic.

* There are some exceptions to this, particularly in children, but detailed discussion of host-adapted serotypes is beyond the scope of this report.

S. enteritidis serotype Paratyphi B probably should be in this category. However, this serotype apparently is less strictly adapted to man than the other microorganisms in the category. Secondary hosts of serotype Paratyphi B include cattle, swine, dogs, and fowl.

In the United States, infections with *S. typhi* and serotypes adapted to man usually occur as sporadic cases and familial outbreaks involving spread to family contacts. They are carrier-borne, and contaminated food usually is involved. However, comparatively few cases are traced to registered carriers. Serotypes Paratyphi A and Paratyphi C do not occur commonly in the United States but are isolated occasionally from persons who have been abroad and acquired the infection. Similarly, serotype Sendai is very rare but might be imported at any time.

2. Serotypes and species of *Salmonella* that are adapted to particular nonhuman animal hosts. Most of these are listed in Table 6, together with data concerning secondary hosts and occurrence in man where known. The primary host of *S. cholerae-suis* undoubtedly is swine.[18] However, this microorganism occurs in other animals (Table 6). Further, it occurs frequently in man, in which instances severe illness (invasion of bloodstream, localizations, high mortality rate) is common, particularly in children.[19, 20]

Although each domestic food animal has its own host-adapted serotype of *Salmonella,* only *S. cholerae-suis* and *S. enteritidis* serotype Dublin are of particular importance in man.

3. Unadapted serotypes of *Salmonella.* These are the bacteria that attack man and other animals with equal facility and that apparently have no host preference. Approximately 1,300 serotypes are now known, but only about 50 or 57 of these occur commonly. These accounted for 96.7 percent of 23,414 cultures from all sources, and 94.8 percent of 12,267 from man, submitted to the National Salmonella Center during the period 1948–1958.[21] Data received from the states during 1967 were given in the Salmonella Summary.[22] This summary showed that 17,977 (91.3 percent) of 19,723 cultures from man belonged to the above-mentioned 50 serotypes. Comparison indicated that, with the exception of changes in rank of some serotypes, the data from these different sources were remarkably similar.

When assigned ranks from 1 to 25 according to their frequency of occurrence, 32 serotypes (including variants such as bioserotype Java and variant Copenhagen) occurred most frequently among cultures submitted to the National Salmonella Center between October 1, 1966, and September 20, 1967.[23] The total number submitted during this particular period was 2,498. The rank of 2,009 (80.4 percent) of these was between 1 and 25, and 72.6 percent of the 2,009 were from humans. Of

TABLE 6 *Salmonella* Adapted to Particular Animal Hosts

Host	Species of Serotype	Secondary Hosts	Man
Fowl	*S. enteritidis* serotype Pullorum	Foxes, swine, dogs, mink	Occurs in children (Ref. 13 and unpublished data) Rare outbreaks in adults[14,15]
	S. enteritidis serotype Gallinarum		Rare isolated case reported[16]
Cattle	*S. enteritidis* serotype Dublin	Other ruminants Foxes (ranch) (Western United States)	Milkborne outbreaks[17] Contamination from infected udders or intestinal excretion
Horses	*S. enteritidis* serotype Abortusequi	None known	Rare outbreaks traced to infected horse meat[18] Also in persons handling aborting mares
Sheep	*S. enteritidis* serotype Abortusovis	None known	
Swine	*S. cholerae-suis*	Cattle (abortion) Fowls Foxes (ranch) Dogs, cats	See text
	S. enteritidis serotype Typhisuis	None known	

the total number (2,498) received, only 58.4 percent ranked among the first 25. However, this figure is greatly influenced by the relatively large number (358 or 14.3 percent) of cultures isolated from river basins and estuaries, which are contaminated heavily by sewage. This information may be compared with that extracted from the Salmonella Surveillance Summaries for the years 1963 through 1967.[22, 24-27] With the exception of occasional changes in rank from year to year, data from the two sources regarding the most commonly occurring salmonellae were in general agreement. Serotypes (including variants) ranked 1 to 25 accounted for approximately 80 percent (average for the five-year period) of isolations from sources other than human and 89 percent of those from humans. These data are presented in tabular form in Appendix A.

With few exceptions the incidence of the serotypes recognized as being of frequent occurrence changes very little from year to year (References 18, 21, 28–31 and Appendix A). However, there have been some notable exceptions to this, as might be expected. For example, serotype Heidelberg was not recognized in the United States until 1955 when it became prominent in fowl. Thereafter this serotype occurred frequently in man and in fowls, and its incidence increased in materials from almost all sources. Serotypes Heidelberg and Infantis have become prevalent and have remained so. Other examples of this are serotypes Blockley and Thompson.[32] However, certain other serotypes of *Salmonella,* such as Hartford, Reading, and Derby, increased suddenly in incidence and subsequently diminished in frequency but have not disappeared entirely. In general, when an uncommon serotype becomes prevalent it remains so, at least for a number of years. The situation regarding serotype Derby is somewhat artificial in that the marked increase in incidence of this serotype during 1963 and 1964 was influenced by intensive investigations of large outbreaks of infection in hospitals, during which many asymptomatic persons were examined.[30, 33, 34] The incidence of serotype Derby has declined since 1964, but it remains relatively common in animals other than fowl.[27] It is of interest to note that most of the above-listed serotypes of *Salmonella* that have become relatively more prominent in recent years have been associated with poultry, chicken eggs, or egg products. The ultimate sources of serotypes Hartford and Reading, the incidence of which increased some years ago and then declined, remains obscure, although serotype Reading occurred in outbreaks in poultry just prior to the sharp increase in incidence of this serotype in man.[35]

In addition to serotype Typhimurium, certain serotypes of *Salmonella* (e.g., serotypes Montevideo, Oranienburg, Newport, Enteritidis, Anatum, and certain others listed in Appendix A) have been known for many years and occur frequently throughout the world.[1, 18, 21, 28, 29, 36]

The large number of characterized serotypes of *Salmonella* should not be a cause for alarm. The majority of these have been described since about 1945,[1, 36] and the large number is considered to be a reflection of the greatly increased number of people who are studying salmonellae, using improved media and methods, and isolating them from a wide variety of sources, sometimes bizarre, most of which previously were not considered or examined. Some of the more recently described serotypes are represented by single isolants, and the ecology of many is not well known.[32, 37] The majority of serotypes that occur commonly in both man and animals belong to the first few O (somatic) antigen groups (References 21, 23, 36 and Appendix A). This has been the experience of numerous investigators but is re-emphasized by the results of a world-wide survey reported by Kelterborn.[36] Among more than 500,000 cultures the distribution was as follows:

Group	Percent
B	47.1
C_1	13.3
C_2	7.1
D_1	23.7
E_2	4.4
	95.6

The serotypes that belonged to the above-mentioned O antigen groups comprised 95.6 percent of the strains, but represented only about 38 percent of all the known serotypes belonging to these O antigen groups. All the remaining serotypes in the Schema constituted only 4.4 percent of total number of cultures analyzed.[36]

The characteristics of disease caused by the unadapted serotypes of *Salmonella* often are cited as follows:

1. Usually produce gastroenteritis rather than enteric fever; infection is localized in the intestine, and bloodstream invasion ordinarily does not occur

2. Short incubation period (probably in part a reflection of dosage)

3. Relatively large dosage of bacteria required to produce illness in healthy adults

In reference to the first statement above, there are many reports in the literature (e.g., References 19, 20, 38, and 39 and references in Chapter 6) of bloodstream invasion and of production of localized lesions in various parts of the body. Some investigators[39] state that a transient bacteremia probably is the rule rather than the exception in febrile individuals. However, these investigators were dealing with hospitalized cases, and as a rule only severely ill persons are admitted to hospitals. Since blood for culture rarely is collected from individuals, febrile or not, exposed and infected in outbreaks of acute salmonellosis, practically nothing is known concerning the incidence of bloodstream invasion outside hospital situations. This point should be investigated whenever conditions are favorable. However, specimens should be taken from representatives of all those exposed, not just from those who exhibit symptoms of salmonellosis. Further, an elevated temperature should not be a criterion for selection, since fever may be caused by dehydration.

The third statement concerning infecting dose is frequently seen in the literature, but it must be qualified. First, a distinction should be made between an *infective dose* of salmonellae and the *dosage required to produce symptoms of salmonellosis in a particular individual* (man or lower animal). Rarely is there an outbreak of salmonellosis in which all exposed individuals develop symptoms. Some of those exposed become infected and excrete the bacteria but are otherwise unaffected, while others develop symptoms of varying degrees of severity. Therefore, the number of bacteria required to produce infection may be smaller than that required to give rise to symptoms of the disease, *but* the numbers required for production of each of these states are dependent on additional factors. These include the age of the host, presence of underlying or debilitating disease, the strain (within a serotype) of *Salmonella* involved, the medium (including food) in which the bacteria may have grown, the degree of gastric acidity, and other factors about which little is known, such as the "natural resistance" of the host to unadapted salmonellae.

Feeding healthy adult human volunteers with salmonellae has provided some information regarding infective dosages and numbers required to produce symptoms of salmonellosis. In one experiment[40] a suspension of serotype Typhimurium in water was fed to five adult subjects before breakfast. Two were fed 2×10^9 organisms. The first of these (age 35) developed slight fever (temperature 38°C) on the third day but did not have diarrhea. The second (age 24) had twelve evacuations and a slight temperature elevation (38°C) on the third day. The other three volunteers received 4×10^9 bacteria each. The first (age 51) of these did not develop fever but had three evacuations on the fourth day. The second (age 44) had five liquid stools on the fourth day, without fever. The last subject (age 30) developed a temperature of 39.6°C and had 15 to 20 liquid stools on the third day and six evacuations on the fourth day (temperature normal). All subjects were normal after the time periods mentioned. Unfortunately, this paper[40] included nothing concerning blood culture or the results of examinations of fecal specimens from the person who did not develop diarrhea (i.e., the first mentioned above, age 35).

In another experiment[41] a single volunteer, 37 years of age, who was normal except for slight constipation, and from whom no salmonellae were isolated, was used. This person was fed serotype Anatum (10^{10}) four hours after a breakfast of bread and milk. The same afternoon the subject experienced abdominal pain and had three semiliquid movements. The following day there was semisolid evacuation. Thereafter the subject's stools reverted to their original consistencies prior to the experiment. Serotype Anatum was recovered from each of the semiliquid stools and from each of ten consecutive specimens obtained daily for ten days, at which time the examinations were terminated.

The work done in 1951[42-45] on experimental human salmonellosis has been quoted widely. It should be noted, however, that the salmonellae employed in these investigations were isolated from purchased samples of spray-dried powdered whole egg. Suspensions of the bacteria were first standardized turbidimetrically and counts of viable organisms were made at the time that calculated dosages were mixed with eggnog. The contaminated eggnog was fed to selected healthy adult male prisoners shortly after the noon meal. Fecal specimens were cultured three times each week for two weeks; thereafter cultures were made weekly until at least three consecutive negative specimens were obtained. Quantification of the numbers of salmonella excreted apparently was not done, and blood cultures were not made. The following serotypes were employed: Meleagridis and Anatum (three strains each), Newport, Derby, and Barielly (one strain each), and four strains of Pullorum.

If the conditions under which the above-mentioned investigations[42-45] were made are borne in mind, a few tentative conclusions may be drawn from the data. In these experiments, infection of some of the subjects was established by ingestion of as few as 12,000 bacteria of serotypes Meleagridis and Anatum. However, the "minimal infective dose" for each of the strains of these two serotypes was not established, since the initial dosages of strains II and III of each were higher (10^6, 158×10^3; 89×10^3, and 159×10^3, respectively). Where more than one strain of a serotype was employed, some strain differences in numbers required to produce clinical illness in these particular subjects were apparent. However, the numbers (125×10^3 to 15×10^6) of these five serotypes of *Salmonella* (excluding serotype Pullorum) that apparently were required to produce salmonellosis in these individuals should not be taken out of context or too literally. Even in some of these subjects, relatively smaller dosages (125×10^3 to 159×10^3) initiated symptoms, and in other individuals, under other circumstances, much smaller numbers might be required. The fact that some subjects were fed second or third dosages of the same strain probably had an effect on the outcome of the experiments. Since serotype Pullorum is host-adapted to fowl, it is not surprising that large numbers (6.8×10^9) were required to produce gastroenteritis. Nevertheless, 1.3×10^9 bacteria of strain II initiated clinical salmonellosis in four of the five subjects fed. The dosage range used with the four strains of serotype Pullorum was 1.3×10^9 to 16×10^9. These numbers of bacteria produced salmonellosis in all except a few of the subjects. The organisms were not recovered from the stools of some of the individuals who were ill, and positive isolations were made during the first or second day only. The media employed were not particularly suitable for the isolation of serotype Pullorum, however. Both convalescent and asymptomatic excretors were produced with all the other serotypes of *Salmonella* employed. Regarding serotype Pullorum, it is fortunate that this serotype is host-adapted, since it is known that some of the procedures used to cook eggs are not adequate to kill salmonellae.[46]

The foregoing comments regarding the experimental work cited above[42-45] emphasize the fact that readers should consult publications directly and not rely wholly upon reviewers' opinions or interpretations. They also emphasize the need for quantitative studies of contaminated foods or products involved in outbreaks whenever this is possible, since data obtained in this way and collected over a period of time should yield more accurate estimates of dosages of salmonellae required to produce disease.*

Some quantitative data of this kind are available, as illustrated by the following examples. Ham was the vehicle of infection in a small outbreak of salmonellosis.[47] Serotype Infantis was present (23,000 per gram) in the ham, as indicated by plate counts on brilliant green agar. The ham was grossly contaminated with other bacteria (250×10^6 total counts) including enterococci, but clostridia were not isolated. In another report, a series of outbreaks were traced to a kind of frozen dessert that contained contaminated frozen egg yolk.[48] In this instance, serotype Typhimurium, bacteriophage type 2a, was the etiological agent. The frozen egg yolk contained approximately 1,100 salmonellae per 100 g, and three 100-g samples of the complete dessert yielded 9, 36, and 150 salmonellae, respectively (average 65 per 100 g or about 0.6 per gram). These estimations were made using the MPN (the most probable number) procedure. Servings of the above-mentioned dessert averaged 75 g; therefore only small numbers of this strain of serotype Typhimurium apparently were required to produce both infection and clinical salmonellosis. Quantitative work also was done with carmine dye that was found to be contaminated with serotype Cubana[49] and that was the vehicle of infection in a hospital-associated outbreak of salmonellosis. Capsules (0.3 g of carmine) contained 30,000 salmonellae. It was reported[49] that as few as 15,000 serotype Cubana organisms produced salmonellosis that sometimes was fatal. Twelve cases were recognized in persons who ingested the dye and became ill with gastroenteritis. Nine

---

* The work of Silverstolpe *et al.* [*J. Appl. Bacteriol., 24* 134 (1961)] should also be mentioned. These investigators reported that small numbers (7 to 14 per g of a strain of serotype Muenchen in contaminated cereal produced illness in infants.

others apparently acquired the disease in the hospital. Most of the 21 cases occurred in infants, debilitated and aged persons, and patients with underlying gastrointestinal disease. About half were children.

Some quantitative work has been done with animal feed and feed ingredients. The most notable is that in which eight-week-old pigs from a herd known to be free of salmonellae were fed naturally contaminated feed.[50] Twenty-four pigs from four litters were used; 20 in the experiment and four as controls. The 20 experimental animals were fed *ad libitum* a diet that contained 10 percent fish meal and 2 percent bone meal. The controls received the same diet, except that the fish and bone meals were omitted. Fecal specimens were examined at intervals throughout the experiment. The animals were killed at intervals, specimens from numerous internal sites were cultured, and serum samples were collected for agglutination tests. After 50 days, feeding of the contaminated diet was discontinued and six remaining pigs were given the same feed as the controls. Two serotypes, Blockley and Orion, were isolated from the fish meal, which contained 50 organisms per 100 g (MPN method). The two serotypes were present in a ratio of 1:10. Using ordinary enrichment procedures, three serotypes of *Salmonella* (Adelaide, Anatum, and Montevideo) were isolated from the bone meal used in the feed (700 per 100 g), but by employing a filtration and centrifugation technique thirteen additional serotypes were recovered. These were serotypes Typhimurium, Stanley, Reading, Derby, Richmond, Tennessee, Newport, Blockley, Meleagridis, Dublin, Portsmouth, Poona, and Cubana. No salmonellae were isolated from the other feed ingredients used. Salmonellae first were demonstrated in the rectum of animals examined postmortem (serotype Reading in one pig after four days), but as time progressed they were isolated with increased frequency from mesenteric lymph nodes (MLN). The numbers of salmonellae in the intestinal contents of seven of the infected pigs were small, as shown by the fact that the bacteria were isolated only after enrichment and by the amounts of tissue that had to be examined (10 g with each of four animals, 2.5 g in one, and 1 g in each of two). After 18 days, serotype Dublin was isolated from MLN of pig No. 7; serotype Typhimurium was recovered from MLN of animals 9 and 12 after 30 and 44 days, respectively. This serotype was also isolated from rectal contents of pig No. 11 at 39 days. Serotype Reading was present in MLN of pig No. 13 after 46 days, and serotype Give was found in rectal and cecal contents of No. 14 at 50 days. Eight days after feeding of the contaminated diet was stopped (total 58 days), serotypes Typhimurium and Give were isolated from MLN of pig No. 15. The results of cultures of fecal specimens made during the experiments are given in Table 7.

TABLE 7   Salmonella Serotypes Isolated from Pigs Fed Naturally Contaminated Feed[a]

Serotype Isolated Pig No.	Days after Beginning of Experiment	No. of Pigs Examined	No. Positive
—	0	20	0
—	0	17	0
—	10	15	0
Not serotyped	14	14	3
Derby, 19	16	14	1
Amager, 11; Anatum, 14	19	13	2
Not serotyped, 8	22	13	1
Not serotyped, 8	25	12	0
Tennessee, 20; Poona, 14	29	12	2
Dublin, 19	32	11	1
Dublin, 19; Enteritidis, 17	36	11	2
Reading, 12; Typhimurium, 11	39	10	2
Derby, 12	43	9	1
Stanley, 19; Anatum, 14	46	8	2
Senftenberg, 19; Give, 14	50	7	2

[a] Adapted from Reference 50.

Salmonellae were not isolated from fecal specimens from the six remaining animals after the contaminated diet was discontinued.

These carefully executed studies[50] are reviewed here because they contain considerable significant information, but the paper should be read in its entirety. Salmonellae were not demonstrated in the feces of the few animals that remained after 50 days and only once in the MLN. However, the results might well have been different had it been possible to transport these pigs some distance and re-examine them at an abattoir.

Two other investigations that yield quantitative data can be cited.[51, 52] In the first,[51] 1,262 samples of feeds, feed ingredients, and fertilizers were examined, and many serotypes of Salmonella, including Typhimurium, were recovered. Quantification (MPN procedure) was done with 69 samples. All estimates of probable numbers were 30 or less per 100 g. As might be expected, the numbers present in finished feeds were less than those in ingredients. Further, the process of pelleting reduced the numbers of salmonellae in the meal or mash employed in these experiments[52] by about 90 percent.

Even though the numbers of salmonellae present in most of the materials examined in the above-mentioned investigations were "low," consideration should be given to the amount of feed consumed by a hog in a day and to the demonstrated[50] cumulative effect of such feedings during the time an animal is being prepared for market.

A review of available literature on the subject indicates that the numbers of salmonellae required to produce infection and to produce symptoms of salmonellosis may be small in many instances and very small in some. Therefore the earlier statement (that a characteristic of disease caused by the unadapted serotypes of *Salmonella* is the relatively large dosage of the organisms required to cause the disease) is but a generality and should be accepted cautiously, especially in view of the paucity of quantitative data on the numbers of salmonellae in foods and products implicated in outbreaks. Most investigated epidemics are traced to foods in which the bacteria may have multiplied. Under these circumstances, the above-mentioned generality may be applicable in epidemics in normal persons (older children and adults). In infants and persons with underlying disease, only small numbers of salmonellae may be required to produce illness, and bloodstream invasion and production of localized lesions are more likely to occur (see Chapter 6).

It is well known that the numbers of salmonellae in certain foods increase greatly when the food is left at room temperature even for short periods of time. Such foods serve as growth media for the bacteria, and even when the numbers of salmonellae initially present are very small, a food item will become heavily contaminated and dangerous if mishandled. Recommended practices regarding such handling of foods as preparation and refrigeration must be followed, particularly in institutions. Otherwise serious consequences can be expected.

Obviously, the aforementioned ecological subdivisions (human adapted, nonhuman adapted, unadapted) are of importance both clinically and epidemiologically. Fortunately, the epidemiology of commonly occurring serotypes of *Salmonella* is fairly well understood. However, little is known concerning either the ecology or the epidemiology of the rarer serotypes, particularly the atypical forms,[30, 31] i.e., the so-called subgenera II and IV of Kauffmann.[3] These atypical salmonellae accounted for only 0.04 percent of more than 86,000 cultures.[1]

APPARENT GENETIC PLASTICITY OF *SALMONELLA**

The question has been posed: What is the significance of the apparent genetic plasticity of the *Salmonella* organism and its multiple serotypes?

* A more detailed discussion with references is given in Appendix B.

So far as disease is concerned, such mutants may affect accurate identification, epidemiology, chemotherapy, and even susceptibility to disinfectants. So far as is now known, genetic changes in cultures of *Salmonella* have little or no effect upon their ability to infect or to produce symptoms of disease. Similarly the very occasional occurrence of biochemical variants does not interfere with characterization of salmonellae by biochemical methods.

The genetic plasticity of salmonellae is more apparent than real, since salmonellae probably are not more or less plastic than other members of the family Enterobacteriaceae (e.g., *Escherichia coli, Shigella, Serratia, Proteus*) or members of other families of bacteria, fungi, and protozoa.

Also, the large number of known serotypes of *Salmonella* is not, *per se,* of great significance to the problem of salmonellosis, since it is well known that relatively few serotypes are involved in a very high percentage of infections in both man and animals throughout the world.

Much of the progress made in bacterial genetics during the past twenty years has involved the use of members of the various genera of Enterobacteriaceae. Because considerable information was already available that dealt with the *natural* variational phenomena of the O (somatic) and H (flagellar) antigens of salmonellae, and because an antigenic schema in which the serotypes could be oriented was available, the potentialities of salmonellae in genetic investigations were quickly recognized. The fact that salmonellae have been studied intensively by many investigators may have given rise to the concept of "apparent genetic plasticity."

Three mechanisms of genetic recombination affect salmonellae, but not salmonellae alone. These are transduction, lysogenic (or phage) conversion, and conjugation. It is evident that the effects of genetic recombination cannot be ignored, especially in serotyping. The roles of the phenomena mentioned in the origin of *Salmonella* serotypes have been the subject of much speculation. Of the mechanisms mentioned, lysogenic conversion probably has the most bearing on serotype identity and epidemiology, since each lysogenized organism undergoes antigenic change.

The effects of genetic change in *Salmonella* do not minimize in any way the value to epidemiology of serological analysis. Exceptional cultures occur rarely, and the salmonellae seen in daily practice ordinarily are perfectly typical in their serological characteristics. Even such organisms as serotype Anatum and serotype Newington, which are lysogenic counterparts, occur separately much more frequently than they do in association.

Similarly, the occurrence of cultures of *Salmonella* that are biochemically atypical is rare, as noted above.[1, 23] Undue attention is perhaps directed to atypical forms because papers get written about them, whereas little is to be said about the thousands of typical strains. Although a single atypical strain may become epidemic and may spread through a hospital or an urban community, it still is but a single strain giving rise to multiple isolations. Further, a strain of serotype Newington that ferments lactose, for example, produces the same symptoms as one that does not.[5]

It seems to be the *rate* at which the changes are effected by various genetic mechanisms that is important to the question of genetic plasticity in *Salmonella*. And many factors affect that rate.

The intent is not to minimize the importance of genetic studies with salmonellae and other bacteria. Quite the contrary, such studies have revealed a great deal about *why* certain variations occur.

Finally, if the known genetic mechanisms that affect the antigenic and biochemical reactions of *Salmonella* and other Enterobacteriaceae took place frequently, classification would be impossible.

THE RESISTANCE (R) FACTORS*

Susceptibility or resistance of *Salmonella* serotypes to various chemotherapeutic agents and their ability to produce bacteriocin-like substances have been used extensively as epidemiological markers in the past. In some instances, at least, this has led to confusion because of the appearance of multiple resistance in strains isolated from animals that were not receiving all the agents for which resistance appeared. No doubt the discrepancies are caused through transfer, by conjugation or transduction, of the genetic materials that regulate the factors in question. In some strains of serotype Typhimurium, resistance to several antibiotics may be transferred as a unit, while in others the resistance factors for certain combinations of drugs may be transferred. Further, genetic transfer of resistance from serotype Typhimurium to *E. coli,* and vice versa, has been demonstrated. Since administration of any of the drugs within the spectrum of resistance of a multiply resistant microorganism may result in its selection and dissemination through suppression of the susceptible flora, some investigators have suggested that it is time to re-examine the entire question of the use of antibiotics and other drugs in the rearing of livestock. Resistance to tetracyclines has increased rapidly in

* A somewhat more detailed account with references is given in Appendix B.

cultures from both man and animals during the past years. Multiply resistant salmonellae, many of which are capable of transferring resistance to such other microorganisms as strains of *E. coli,* have been reported in the United States.

Current data indicate that R factors occur only in gram-negative bacteria. These episomal factors are responsible for development of multiple resistance of microorganisms to antimicrobial agents. Transfer of R factors takes place primarily through conjugation. Fertile (F+) cells are required and when Hfr (high-frequency) donor cells are present, recombination and transfer of episomal material proceeds at a rapid rate. Transfer of the episomal R factor material from cell to cell takes place through pili, the presence of which also is genetically controlled. If there is a repression of the pilus gene, transfer of drug resistance does not occur. There are at least two naturally occurring R factors.[13]

Studies have indicated that transfer of R factors is mediated by an episomal transfer factor. Transfer of R factors in nature is limited by the rate of conjugation and by the rare chance of contact between cells that possess the transfer factor and cells that possess resistance factors. However, when a drug is introduced into a heterogeneous population of gram-negative bacteria, selective pressure ("antibiotic pressure") is exerted upon the population. This selection produces greater opportunity for contact between cells that possess the transfer factor and those with R factor. Hence, this pressure facilitates the selection and development of multiply resistant strains of bacteria, which then may become predominant. This occurs in hospitals and other institutional situations. It also occurs in animals under analogous circumstances, as shown by Anderson.[53]

USE OF ANTIBIOTICS IN ANIMAL PRODUCTION

Since about 1950,[54] antibiotics have been added to animal feeds and feed supplements. This practice was begun because of the reported (e.g., Reference 55) growth-promoting effect of certain antibiotics, particularly in poultry and swine. In the intervening years there has been considerable argument between proponents of the use of antibiotics in feeds for the above-mentioned reason and those who oppose their use because of the development of antibiotic-resistant salmonellae and other bacteria in the tissues and intestinal tracts of animals (e.g., References 53, 56, and 57) and the consequent potential hazard to public health. The question of the effects of residues of antibiotics in meat and edible viscera from animals fed antibiotics in their feeds has not been resolved. Some investigators[58] have found no evidence of harm caused by residues of antibiotics in chickens resulting from their being fed "low levels" in their feed. Adherents of this school of thought believe that although there is a "potential" hazard from the emergence of resistant salmonellae, the over-all advantages of feeding "low levels" of antibiotics warrant continuing the practice. Other investigators[58] have argued (a) that caution should be exercised in the use of antibiotics in feeds, (b) that feeding of "low levels" of antibiotics results in the emergence of resistant bacteria, but at a slower rate than where "high levels" are employed, and (c) that the development of resistant salmonellae in cattle is directly proportional to the amount of tetracycline in the diet.

The various "levels" of antibiotics employed in feeds and feed supplements need to be defined more clearly. The largest amount listed in guidelines published in 1952[54] was 40 g per ton. However, it has been reported[19] that reduction in cost of antibiotics has led to increase in the level used in feeds for animals, for example, from 40–50 g per ton to 60–80 g per ton. Others[58] state that the levels of antibiotics currently employed are as follows:

low level	10 to 49 g per ton (feed supplement)
medium level	50 to 100 g per ton (prophylaxis)
high level	150 or more g per ton (therapeutic)

A review of the literature on the addition of antibiotics to animal feed or water, and of R factors, indicates that as *currently practiced* the addition of antibiotics to feeds is causing undesirable changes in the balance between host and pathogen.

The use of antibiotics in feeds for prophylaxis or for growth promotion of animals incurs two possible hazards to man, namely, allergy in response to the presence of drug residues in food and changes of the flora of animals, making possible emergence of drug-resistant clones. The latter may serve as a source of antibiotic-resistant pathogens for man. So far as salmonellosis is concerned, the emergence of drug-resistant strains may pose a potential problem for the effective treatment of systemic salmonellosis, though not for salmonella food poisoning or gastroenteritis. In over-all consideration of bacterial infections of man, the use in feeds of *only truly low levels* of antibiotics for growth-promoting purposes should be permitted. If subsequent experience and research indicate that these levels are not safe or that genetic change is not at an acceptably low rate, such permission should be rescinded. The routine use of prophylactic levels of antibiotics in feeds should not be permitted[53] (see also Appendix B).

REFERENCES

1. W. H. Ewing and M. M. Ball, "The Biochemical Reactions of Members of the Genus *Salmonella*," *NCDC Publ.*,* Atlanta, Ga. (1966).
2. W. H. Ewing, "Revised Definitions for the Family Enterobacteriaceae, Its Tribes and Genera," *NCDC Publ.*, Atlanta, Ga. (1967).
3. F. Kauffmann, "The Bacteriology of Enterobacteriaceae," Einar Munksgaard, Copenhagen, Denmark. (Williams & Wilkens, Baltimore, Md.) (1966).
4. W. J. Martin, W. H. Ewing, A. M. Murlin, and S. Bartes, "Biochemical Reactions of *Salmonella*" (in press).
5. Salmonella Surveillance Rep. No. 57, *NCDC Publ.*, Atlanta, Ga. (1967).
6. W. J. Martin and W. H. Ewing, "Isolation of *Salmonella* from Foods and Food Products," *NCDC Publ.*, Atlanta, Ga. (1967).
7. W. H. Ewing, "An Outline of Nomenclature for the Family Enterobacteriaceae," *Int. Bull. Bacteriol. Nomencl. Taxon.*, *13*, 95 (1963).
8. W. H. Ewing, "Enterobacteriaceae: Taxonomy and Nomenclature," *NCDC Publ.*, Atlanta, Ga. (1966).
9. Subcommittee on Enterobacteriaceae, American Society for Microbiology, Rep. in *ASM News*, *30*, 22 (1964).
10. Subcommittee on Enterobacteriaceae, American Society for Microbiology, Rep. in *ASM News*, *34*, 30 (1968).
11. Salmonella Committee of Nomenclature Committee, International Society for Microbiology, Rep. in *J. Hyg.*, *34*, 333 (1934).
12. P. R. Edwards and W. H. Ewing, *Identification of Enterobacteriaceae*, 2nd ed. Burgess Publishing Co., Minneapolis, Minn. (1962).
13. R. W. Ten Bensel and L. P. Williams, Jr., "A Bizarre Terminal Event in a Case of Granulomatous Disease of Childhood," *Minn. Med. 49*, 580 (1966).
14. R. B. Mitchell, F. C. Garlock, and R. H. Broh-Kahn, "An Outbreak of Gastroenteritis Presumably Caused by *Salmonella pullorum*," *J. Infec. Dis.*, *79*, 57, (1946).
15. T. F. Judefind, "Report of a Relatively Severe and Protracted Diarrhea Presumedly due to *S. pullorum* from the Ingestion of Incompletely Cooked Eggs," *J. Bacteriol. 54*, 667 (1947).
16. L. Popp, "Fowl Typhoid Organisms as Cause of Gastroenteritis in Man," *Med. Klin.*, 135 (1946); Abstr. *J. Amer. Vet. Med. Ass.*, *111*, 314 (1947).
17. R. J. Schroeder and M. B. Dale, "*Salmonella dublin* from Cows Contaminates Market Milk," *J. Amer. Vet. Med. Ass.*, *136*, 161 (1960).
18. P. R. Edwards, D. W. Bruner, and A. B. Moran, *The Genus* Salmonella: *Its Occurrence and Distribution in the United States*, Bull. No. 525, Ky. Agr. Exp. Sta., Univ. Ky., Lexington (1948).
19. E. Neter, "*Salmonella cholerae suis* (Weldin) Bacteremia," *Amer. J. Dis. Child.*, *64*, 255 (1942).
20. I. Saphra and M. Wassermann, "*Salmonella cholerae suis*. A Clinical and Epidemiological Evaluation of 329 Infections Identified between 1940 and 1954 in the New York Salmonella Center," *Amer. J. Med. Sci.*, *228*, 525 (1954).

* NCDC, National Communicable Disease Center, Atlanta, Georgia 30333.

21. P. R. Edwards, pp. 7 to 12, in *Salmonellosis—Proc. Nat. Conf. Salmonellosis,** Pub. Health Serv. Publ. No. 1262, NCDC Publ., Atlanta, Ga. (1965).

22. Annual Summary, Salmonella Surveillance, 1967, NCDC Publ., Atlanta, Ga. (1968).

23. W. J. Martin and W. H. Ewing, "Prevalence of Serotypes of *Salmonella*" *Appl. Microbiol., 17,* 111 (1969).

24. Annual Summary, Salmonella Surveillance, 1963, NCDC Publ., Atlanta, Ga. (1964).

25. Annual Summary, Salmonella Surveillance, 1964, NCDC Publ., Atlanta, Ga. (1965).

26. Annual Summary, Salmonella Surveillance, 1965, NCDC Publ., Atlanta, Ga. (1966).

27. Annual Summary, Salmonella Surveillance, 1966, NCDC Publ., Atlanta, Ga. (1967).

28. P. R. Edwards and D. W. Bruner, "The Occurrence and Distribution of *Salmonella* Types in the United States," *J. Infec. Dis., 72,* 58 (1943).

29. A. B. Moran, C. D. Van Houweling, and E. M. Ellis, "The Results of Typing Salmonella from Animal Sources in the United States," *Conf. Proc., 33* (1965).

30. J. R. Boring, "The Field Studies," *Conf. Proc.,* 122 (1965).

31. E. van Oye, ed., "World Problem of Salmonellosis," Dr. W. Junk, The Hague, The Netherlands (1964).

32. P. R. Edwards and M. M. Galton, "Salmonellosis," *Advan. Vet. Sci. 11,* 1 (1967).

33. E. Sanders, F. J. Sweeney, Jr., E. A. Friedman, J. R. Boring, E. L. Randall, and L. D. Polk, "An Outbreak of Hospital-Associated Infections due to *Salmonella derby,*" *J. Amer. Med. Ass., 186,* 984 (1963).

34. F. J. Sweeney and E. L. Randall, "Clinical and Epidemiological Studies of *Salmonella derby* Infections in a General Hospital," *Conf. Proc.,* 130 (1965).

35. R. H. Drachman, N. J. Petersen, J. R. Boring, and F. J. Payne, "Widespread *Salmonella reading* Infection of Undetermined Origin," *Pub. Health Rep., 73,* 885 (1958).

36. E. Kelterborn, "*Salmonella* Species," Dr. W. Junk, The Hague, Netherlands (1967).

37. R. Rohde, "The Identification, Epidemiology, and Pathogenicity of the Salmonellae of Subgenus II," *J. Appl. Bacteriol. 28,* 368 (1965).

38. E. Neter, "Observations on the Transmission of Salmonellosis in Man," *Amer. J. Pub. Health, 40,* 929 (1950).

39. I. Saphra and J. W. Winter, "Clinical Manifestations of Salmonellosis in Man," *N. Engl. J. Med., 256,* 1128 (1957).

40. E. Hormaeche, C.-A. Peluffo, and P.-L. Aleppo, "Nueva Contribución al Estudio Etiológico de las 'Diarreas Infantiles de Verano'," *Arch. Urug. Med., 9,* 113 (1936).

41. G. Varela and J. Olarte, "Infección Experimental del Hombre con *Salmonella anatum,*" *Medicina, Mexico, 22,* 57 (1942).

42. N. B. McCullough and C. W. Eisele, "Experimental Human Salmonellosis. I. Pathogenicity of Strains of *Salmonella Meleagridis* and *Salmonella Anatum* Obtained from Spray-dried Whole Egg," *J. Infec. Dis., 88,* 278 (1951).

* Abbreviated "Conf. Proc." hereinafter.

43. N. B. McCullough and C. W. Eisele, "II. Immunity Studies Following Experimental Illness with *Salmonella meleagridis* and *Salmonella anatum,*" *J. Immunol., 66,* 595 (1951).
44. N. B. McCullough and C. W. Eisele, "III. Pathogenicity of Strains of *Salmonella Newport, Salmonella Derby,* and *Salmonella Bareilly* Obtained from Spray-dried Whole Egg," *J. Infec. Dis., 89,* 209 (1951).
45. N. B. McCullough and C. W. Eisele, "IV. Pathogenicity of Strains of *Salmonella Pullorum* Obtained from Spray-dried Whole Egg," *J. Infec. Dis., 89,* 259 (1951).
46. A. Beloian and G. C. Schlosser, "Adequacy of Cooking Procedures for the Destruction of Salmonellae," *Amer. J. Pub. Health, 53,* 782 (1963).
47. R. Angelotti, G. C. Bailey, M. J. Foter, and K. H. Lewis, "*Salmonella infantis* Isolated from Ham in Food Poisoning Incident," *Pub. Health Rep., 76,* 771 (1961).
48. Salmonella Surveillance Report No. 61 (and supplement dated Oct. 23, 1967), NCDC Publ., Atlanta, Ga. (1967).
49. D. J. Lang, L. J. Kunz, A. R. Martin, S. A. Schroeder, and L. A. Thomson, "Carmine as a Source of Nosocomial Salmonellosis," *N. Engl. J. Med., 276,* 829 (1967).
50. H. W. Smith, "The Effect of Feeding Pigs on Food Naturally Contaminated with Salmonellae," *J. Hyg., 58,* 381 (1960).
51. Working Party of the Public Health Laboratory Service, Rep. in *Mon. Bull. Minn. Health, 18,* 26 (1959).
52. "*Salmonella* Organisms in Animal Feeding Stuffs," Rep. in *Mon. Bull. Minn. Health Lab. Serv., 20,* 73 (1961).
53. E. S. Anderson, "Facteurs de transfert et résistance aux antibiotiques chez les entérobacteries," *Ann. Inst. Pasteur, 112,* 547 (1967).
54. U.S. Department of Agriculture, "The Use of Vitamin B₁₂ and Antibiotic Supplements in Livestock Feeding," A.H.D. Rep. No. 145, Washington, D.C. (1952).
55. R. J. Lillie, J. R. Sizemore, and H. R. Bird, "Environment and Stimulation of Growth of Chicks by Antibiotics," *Poult. Sci., 32,* 466 (1953).
56. J. S. Garside, R. F. Gordon, and J. F. Tucker, "The Emergence of Resistant Strains of *Salmonella typhimurium* in the Tissues and Alimentary Tracts of Chickens Following the Feeding of an Antibiotic," *Res. Vet. Sci., 1,* 184 (1960).
57. B. C. Hobbs, J. C. Reeves, J. S. Garside, R. F. Gordon, E. M. Barnes, D. H. Shrimpton, and E. S. Anderson, "Antibiotic Treatment of Poultry in Relation to *Salmonella typhimurium,*" *Mon. Bull. Minn. Health, 19,* 178 (1960).
58. *The Use of Drugs in Animal Feeds: Proceedings of a Symposium,* NAS Publ. 1679, National Academy of Sciences, Washington, D.C. (1969).

6 How Man Becomes Infected

In this chapter only the unadapted serotypes of *Salmonella*, i.e., those that exhibit no apparent host adaptations or preferences, will be considered, since these are the serotypes that commonly cause salmonellosis in man and animals.

OCCURRENCE AND TRANSMISSION OF UNADAPTED *SALMONELLA*

MAN

In discussing the transmission of the commonly occurring serotypes of *Salmonella* in man, it is necessary to consider first the role of the carrier and second the animal reservoirs of the bacteria.

There is in the literature much evidence pointing to the importance of the human carrier in the transmission of salmonellosis. Formerly, it was thought that persons with gastroenteritis caused by unadapted serotypes of *Salmonella* excreted the bacteria in large numbers while symptomatic, and that the causative agents persisted in the intestine only for short periods after symptoms disappeared. There was little information on the role of the symptomless excretor who had no history of intestinal infection. It is now known that some convalescents, as well as persons without history of symptoms, may excrete salmonellae for long periods. This is not to imply that most such persons are permanent carriers, as is the case with those who excrete *S. typhi* because of chronic infection of the biliary or urinary tract. Occasionally cultures of *Salmonella* are isolated from gallstones, as *S. typhi* so often is, and the persons from whom these stones were removed were undoubtedly permanent carriers. It is clear that permanent carriers of unadapted salmonellae are rare, however, probably representing a small percentage of those persons in whom bloodstream invasion occurred.

Conversely, the long-term carrier state (six months or more) following disease occurs more often than is commonly realized. Many investigators[1-19] have reported on the frequency of long-term carriers, particularly among children, on familial spread from such carriers, and on the fact that excretion of the bacteria is intermittent. An extreme instance has been cited in which an adult carried serotype Bovismorbificans for six years.[16]

Similarly, the literature is replete with references to asymptomatic carriers who have no history of diarrheal disease (e.g., References 20–24). Many of these asymptomatic excretors of salmonellae have been discovered through routine examination of fecal specimens from food handlers. Estimates[20-23] of the numbers of carriers in various countries are available (range, 2–50 per thousand), but it should be recalled that in the majority of asymptomatic carriers, the bacteria persist for relatively short periods of time and excretion of salmonellae is intermittent.[15, 23] Single examinations of Bantu schoolchildren[23] indicated that 7.5 percent were carrying salmonellae, but examination of a series of seven specimens collected over a period of a year revealed that a cumulative total of 35.5 percent were positive at least once during the year. Hence, carrier rate figures based upon single examinations do not accurately reflect the percentage of a population that may be asymptomatic carriers of salmonellae at some point during a year. When repeat examinations are made, the cumulative total of isolates is greatly increased.[14, 15, 23] Certain professional food handlers, including caterers, apparently have not been examined in longitudinal-time studies; but such investigations should be made, since the carrier rate among food handlers is generally higher than among persons in other occupations.[18, 24, 25] Carriers among the employees of one catering firm were responsible for several outbreaks of salmonellosis (serotype Thompson) in Louisiana and Texas (unpublished data).

The presence of host-adapted salmonellae such as *S. typhi* and serotype Paratyphi A, as well as shigellae, in market meats[26] from areas of high endemicity emphasizes the role of the human carrier in contamination of food and transmission of salmonellae. This role is further underscored by such episodes as outbreaks of salmonellosis caused by serotype Newport traced to smoked fish[27] and serotype Miami in watermelon,[28] i.e., foods in which salmonellae are not indigenous. Contaminated dried yeast, milk substitute made from soybean flour, dried coconut, and synthetic cream topping also have been vehicles of transmission in epidemics of salmonellosis.

Thus there are several classes of carriers or excretors of unadapted serotypes of *Salmonella* among humans: permanent (rare); long-term asymptomatic; short-term, either convalescent or asymptomatic; and active cases. Persons become asymptomatic carriers through having had the disease or from exposure to infection without development of symptoms. The duration of the carrier state is variable in different age groups in both man and lower animals. In persons with acute gastroenteritis, the bacteria are excreted in large numbers,[29] but as most such patients recover, the numbers of salmonellae excreted diminishes, so that after three or four weeks the bacteria usually cannot be demonstrated in stools. A few, however, continue to excrete salmonellae for much longer periods,[1,3,5,9,12,14,15,22,30,31] i.e., for weeks or months and occasionally for several years. It should be noted that the carrier state may be longer in enteric fever caused by salmonellae such as serotype Paratyphi B.[30] Careful quantitative work[29-32] has shown that the number of salmonellae excreted by some carriers is great, at least in the case of serotype Paratyphi B,[32] but that excretion is intermittent.

As might be expected the carrier rate is higher among food handlers[18, 33-36] than it is in the general population in the United States. Further, it is known that workers in abattoirs, for example, may carry salmonellae to their homes and subsequently infect members of their families who, in turn, infect familial contacts.[37] Similarly, workers in processing plants handling dried, powdered materials, as well as employees in bakeries, and caterers may be important in the transmission of salmonellae.[38-40]

Infants frequently become long-term carriers and may harbor the bacteria for longer periods than older persons.[2, 5, 6] Further, they transmit infection to other members of their families.

It has been demonstrated[41-47] that salmonellae occur in the upper respiratory tract before the onset of gastrointestinal symptoms, and that transmission of infection may be airborne. Since salmonellae have been isolated from dust,[35] this possible route of transmission should be investigated thoroughly. Transient upper respiratory infections might occur among employees in certain processing plants because of their exposure to dust or aerosols containing small numbers of salmonellae. Also, there is need for more critical investigation, including quantitative work, of upper respiratory specimens from patients and from the several classes of carriers mentioned. Comparable studies in outbreaks caused by the same and different serotypes of salmonellae might shed light on differences between strains of the same serotype.

Finally, active cases of salmonellosis in man are sources of contamination and transmission to other human beings and to lower animals. Infection of one person by another may occur in a variety of ways. Transmission may be direct by means of the fecal to oral route, it may be airborne,[35, 41-48] and it may be indirect by means of foods, toys, towels, contaminated toilet seats, and many other objects. All these avenues of transmission may occur in the household, between families, in restaurants, and in institutions including hospitals.[6, 19, 22, 46-56] Instances of transmission of unadapted salmonellae from man to animals are known (Reference 57 and unpublished data). Also, the highly host-adapted *S. typhi* and serotype Paratyphi A have occasionally been isolated from animals such as sheep, horses, dogs, chickens, and hogs (Reference 11 and unpublished data). Although such instances are rare, the distinct possibility remains that if these host-adapted salmonellae can be transmitted to lower animals, transmission of unadapted serotypes of salmonellae may be more frequent.

Discharge of salmonellae in pus from fistula of the arm with periostitis, from pulmonary lesions, and from otitis media has been reported.[44-46, 48] Salmonellae might easily be transmitted directly, or by air, from such drainages. For discussion of other more unusual aspects of salmonellosis see References 35, 44, and 58–62.

The presence of salmonellae in nurseries constitutes an important problem. More often than not transmission in hospital nurseries results from careless practices. Infections may be introduced into nurseries by a variety of means, e.g., by infants born of mothers who are preclinical or active cases, convalescent, or asymptomatic carriers.[46, 63-67] Transfer of infants from the nursery of one hospital to that of another also has led to outbreaks.[7, 53, 68, 69] In one instance, two babies with diarrhea were found to be infected with *Salmonella* and were promptly removed from the nursery, and the nursery was closed. No further cases developed. However, the infected infants were placed in isolation in a room adjacent to rooms housing premature babies. Seven cases developed among the latter, and three fatalities resulted. In another hospital, a series of unrelated cases of obscure origin occurred. Subsequent investigation revealed that the lawn of the hospital had been fertilized with dried activated sludge, and from it were isolated the same serotypes of *Salmonella* that had been found in the patients (unpublished data). More thoughtful management would have prevented these infections.

Contamination of objects in delivery rooms and nurseries may also give rise to outbreaks. Transmission of salmonellosis by infected resuscitators in the delivery rooms of two hospitals has been reported,[70] and salmonellosis has been transmitted through the agency of a water bath, used to warm formula bottles,[66] found to have been contaminated by an electrician who repaired it and who was an asymptomatic carrier. These examples serve to illustrate the numerous pathways by which enteric pathogens may gain entrance to nurseries and emphasize the need for frequent sterilization of all equipment. It is apparent that in the investigation of enteric infections in nurseries, every person and object with which infants come into direct or indirect contact must be regarded with suspicion.

WARM-BLOODED ANIMALS

Fowl

The frequency with which salmonellae are isolated from domestic fowl indicates that these animals probably constitute the largest single reservoir of these bacteria.[11, 57, 71-86] Of approximately 25,000 cultures isolated from animals in the United States during the last 30 years, more than two thirds were recovered from domestic fowl.[11, 72-74, 84, 85] Since bacteriological examination of fowl is made more frequently than of other animals, it is impossible to determine precisely the relative incidence of salmonella infection. Salmonellosis has been recognized as a significant disease in poultry for about five decades. It usually occurs as an acute disease in fowl less than a month old. Mortality rates vary from 0 to more than 80 percent.[81] It is generally agreed that if the disease exists in breeding flocks, it will eventually cause problems such as impaired egg production, lowered fertility and hatchability, and higher mortality in chicks hatched. The disease may also cause stunting and debilitation that increases susceptibility to other diseases.[85] Typhimurium is the serotype of Salmonella most commonly isolated from fowl, but many other serotypes are recovered; and the majority of these are also found in man. Transmission of infection in fowl may be ovarian or by means of intestinal contents. Parenthetically, chicks sold at Eastertime have been a source of infection in children (References 87 and 88 and unpublished data), as have imported stuffed ducklings (unpublished data).

Cattle

Salmonellosis in cattle is caused primarily by serotypes Dublin and Typhimurium, but more than 75 other serotypes have been encountered, the most common of which are Newport, Enteritidis, Anatum, Heidelberg, and Panama. In recent years, enteritis in dairy and beef cattle caused by salmonellae has increased.[24, 89] The highest incidence of disease apparently is between September and March,[90, 91] which suggests that the probability of transmission is greater during the winter months when the animals are quartered together. The literature on the subject of salmonellosis in cattle has been reviewed elsewhere[24, 40, 47, 74, 78, 92-97] and will not be expanded upon here. Suffice it to say that the effect of transport and holding on the prevalence of salmonellae in cattle has been studied.[90, 97] In one investigation,[90] the mean infection rate in calves on the farm was estimated at 0.5 percent; it increased to nearly 36 percent after the animals were kept in holding pens for two to five days. Salmonellae are found in lymph nodes and in feces of cattle,[40] and transmission by means of fecal contamination can occur, especially when the animals are crowded.

Sheep

Serotypes of *Salmonella* have been isolated from outbreaks of enteritis[98] and of abortion[99] in sheep. A variety of serotypes have been recovered from sheep[11] and from mutton.[100]

Swine

S. cholerae-suis is most frequently associated with enteritis in swine. However, when otherwise normal animals are slaughtered, the serotypes found most frequently are usually the same as those commonly isolated from man. This suggests either transmission from one to the other or common sources of origin.[101] The occurrence of certain serotypes in swine and the same serotypes in feeds and feed ingredients indicates the latter as important sources of infection.[101] Direct transmission of infection in swine takes place readily through fecal contamination of their surroundings.

The occurrence of salmonellae in the lymph glands of hogs was demonstrated in 1939[102] and has since been confirmed by many investigators.[4] As in cattle, there is a great increase in the demonstrable prevalence of salmonellae in swine from the time they leave the farm and arrive at abattoirs.[103-106] Spread of infection continues while the animals are kept in holding lots. Upon arrival in abattoirs, swine rarely show clinical signs of salmonellosis, but each infected animal provides a source for transmission, resulting in contamination of pork products available to the consumer.

The importance of intravital infection in the above-mentioned food animals should not be overlooked. The occurrence of salmonellae in the intestinal contents of these animals is not the only source of contamination. Salmonellae may be present in lymph nodes and internal organs of otherwise normal animals, as well as those that are ill. This may lead to contamination of abattoirs, foods, feeds, etc. Hence, every effort should be made to control the spread of salmonellae among these animals at the producer level, as well as in abattoirs, rendering plants, and the like.

Horses

In recent years, outbreaks of enteritis with high mortality rates have been reported in several states,[96, 107, 108] and in one instance the same serotype of *Salmonella* was isolated from a fatal case of enteritis and from cottonseed meal fed to the horses.[96] Development of enteritis in normal horses during transportation ("shipping fever") also occurs (unpublished data, 1947 and Reference 11). A variety of serotypes of *Salmonella* are known to occur in enteritis in horses, among which are Typhimurium, Newport, and Anatum. Although horsemeat is not commonly consumed by man in the United States, it is an important constituent of feeds for dogs, cats, ranch mink, foxes, and other animals. These animals may in turn transmit infection to man.

Dogs and Cats

At least as early as 1938 it was demonstrated that cats and dogs can be carriers of salmonellae.[109-111] More recently, several investigators reported the occurrence and prevalence of serotypes of *Salmonella* in household pets, particularly dogs and cats.[112-121] In one instance, in which sixteen serotypes of *Salmonella* were found in 18 of 100 dogs, rejected eggs fed to the animals apparently were the source of infection.[114] Among 1,626 normal household dogs and 73 normal cats, 15 and 12 percent, respectively, were excreting salmonellae.[116] The prevalence of infection among kennel dogs was much higher (68 percent of 572 animals). Annual minimal attack rates, based on monthly cultural findings, exceeded 600 per 100 dogs per annum, an average of one infection every two months.[117] Transmission of infection from dog to dog, and from man and other animals to dogs, may take place directly because of the coprophagic habits of dogs. Transmission to dogs also occurs by means of their feeds—either dried, cubed feed[119] or frozen horsemeat.[120] Infection of children by dogs has occurred.[40]

Rodents

For many years it was assumed that rodents were frequent carriers only of serotypes Typhimurium and Enteritidis, but it is now known that wild rats may excrete a variety of serotypes, although cultural surveys[122] usually indicate a low carrier rate. However, it is known that prevalence may increase when the rat population in rendering plants increases, and that the serotypes of *Salmonella* carried usually are the same as those present in their environment.[123] Further, salmonellae may remain viable in the feces of rodents for a year or more. Small rodents, such as mice and hamsters, may be infected and transmit infection to humans.[124]

Other Warm-Blooded Animals

Serotypes of *Salmonella* have been isolated from a great many animal species in addition to those just mentioned,[11] e.g., mink, ferrets,[125] and wild animals including marsupials[126, 127] and bats.[128]

COLD-BLOODED ANIMALS

Reptiles

The occurrence of salmonellae in snakes, turtles, and lizards has been known for many years.[112, 129, 130] Evidence indicates that snakes are involved in the transmission of salmonellosis in turkeys[110] at least, and probably in other domestic fowl as well. Various serotypes of *Salmonella* have been recovered from both snakes and turtles, in the latter, both in captivity and in their natural habitats. Attention has been directed to turtles in recent years, because it is known that salmonellae may be transmitted from pet turtles to children and thence to other family members [131, 132] Young turtles sold as pets apparently are hatched and raised in highly contaminated ponds. The breeder animals and the young are fed a wide variety of refuse, animal by-products, and meat scraps, all of which are likely to be contaminated with salmonellae. Further, the conditions under which these animals are kept in retail stores frequently are highly unsanitary. Measures should be adopted to control this source of transmission of salmonellosis.

Insects and Ticks

That flies carry salmonellae has been known for many years.[133] How important they are in transmitting salmonellosis has never been clear. However, contamination of flies in abattoirs has been demonstrated, and tagged flies have been found as far as three miles from their origin.[134] Hence flies may play some role in the spread of infection, particularly in highly endemic areas.[24] Dried flies and other insects are commonly used as feed for pet turtles. Roaches also have been reported to harbor salmonellae.[24] The importance of their role in the transmission of salmonellae is not known with certainty, but they are potentially dangerous in this respect, particularly, it would seem, in abattoirs, processing plants, and food establishments. Salmonellae also have been isolated from fleas,[135] lice,[136] and ticks.[137]

OCCURRENCE AND TRANSMISSION OF SALMONELLA IN FOODS AND FEEDS

FOODS FOR MAN

The widespread distribution of salmonellae in animals used for food frequently results in contamination of human foods derived from these animals. Contaminated poultry, meats, egg products, and pork and beef products are often associated with outbreaks of salmonellosis. Investigations also have revealed salmonellae in a miscellaneous variety of processed foods. Some of these foods contain a contaminated ingredient of animal origin; others, such as contaminated coconut, cereals, yeast, and protein concentrates prepared from cottonseed and soybeans, are of plant origin.

Eggs and Egg Products

The attention of health authorities and the general public in the United States was first forcibly directed to the problem of salmonellosis when eggs and egg products were incriminated in epidemics of the disease. Salmonellae may gain entrance into eggs by ovarian infection or by penetrating the shell. The prevalance of salmonellae in, or on, the shell of Grade A eggs is low, but one infected egg can contaminate a large batch of commercially processed egg product. When temperatures during processing permit (22°C or above), salmonellae multiply. This became apparent during World War II, when salmonellae were found in 10 percent of the spray-dried egg samples imported into England from the United States, Canada, and Argentina.[138] Twenty-two of the 33 serotypes recovered had not previously been found in Great Britain. Concurrently, an 85 percent increase in annual incidence of food-borne infections caused by salmonellae was observed, much of this increase being attributed to dried eggs. In the United States, salmonellae were isolated from 1,810 (34.8 percent) of 5,198 samples of, presumably, unpasteurized spray-dried whole egg powder.[139] Fresh shell eggs, as well as frozen and dried eggs, have been implicated in numerous outbreaks of salmonella infection in man.[140-142] Canned dried egg yolk prepared from pasteurized liquid yolk was the vehicle in a widespread epidemic of salmonellosis in infants.[143]

Salmonellae have been isolated from a variety of prepared cake and bread mixes containing egg or egg albumen.[144, 145] More than 50 percent of the samples of some lots of cake mix were contaminated with types that occur frequently in man in the United States and Canada. Meringue prepared from frozen or dried egg white has been implicated in numerous epidemics of salmonellosis (References 100 and 146 and unpublished data).

Meats and Meat Products

Papers published as long ago as 1888 and 1894[147, 148] demonstrated that contaminated beef can be the source of salmonellosis in man. Also, it has long been known that fresh pork and beef products are often contaminated.[97, 149-150] Investigations in Florida[150] revealed that contamination of fresh pork sausage ranged from 8 percent in samples from national producers to 58 percent in those from local abattoirs. Similarly high rates of contamination of fresh and processed pork, beef, and mutton have been reported in Europe and elsewhere.[97, 100]

The wide distribution of salmonellae in fresh poultry has been demonstrated in numerous investigations (e.g., References 151–154). Indications are that contamination is carried over into processed, partially cooked, or "ready-to-eat" poultry products, or that the products are recontaminated after the heating process. An extensive outbreak in Georgia[88] was caused by serotype Blockley in commercially prepared chicken salad. Numerous outbreaks have been attributed to turkey meat that was insufficiently roasted, or recontaminated after roasting.[155] Prepared turkey rolls have been implicated in numerous outbreaks.[146, 156]

One infected animal or bird entering a processing plant can become the source of contamination for products from that plant. In turn, such products can contaminate other foods with which they come in contact or the environment in which other foods are prepared. Further, persons handling these products may become infected. Examination of employees in an abattoir and meat-processing plants in Costa Rica revealed salmonellae in 20 percent.[157] During studies of the abattoir employees, office employees, and their families, it was found that the highest rate of infection was among the families of abattoir workers.[158]

Milk and Milk Products

Raw or improperly pasteurized milk and milk products from animals may be contaminated with salmonellae and have been incriminated in many large outbreaks of salmonellosis in the United States and elsewhere.[40, 159, 160] Cows rarely excrete salmonellae in their milk except during the febrile period of acute salmonellosis, but fecal contamination by carrier animals occurs frequently.

Powdered dry milk may contain salmonellae and has been implicated in salmonellosis.[161,162] Cheese made from raw or improperly pasteurized milk has been reported as the vehicle of transmission of salmonellae on many occasions.[163-166]

Miscellaneous Foods

A wide variety of foods and food products, including vegetables, have been incriminated from time to time as the mode of transmission of salmonellae. Some are listed below:

Dried yeast used as a dietary supplement[167,168]

Milk substitute made from soybeans (A. S. Browne, personal communication, 1954)

Dried cereal[169]

Smoked fish[27,170,171]

Dried coconut[172,173]

Sauces and salad dressings[146,174]

Bakery products, cakes, rolls, etc., many with egg[146]

Cream-filled desserts and toppings[38,146,175]

Cake mixes[146]

Bread and bread mixes[38,146]

Gelatin[176]

Synthetic ice cream[177]

Pickles[178]

Sandwiches of various kinds, commercially prepared and often sold in vending machines[179,180]

Since salmonellae are not indigenous to many of the listed items, the importance of the processing plant in the transmission of salmonellosis is re-emphasized.

The role of vegetables, particularly those used in salads, should not be overlooked.[100] How often vegetables are involved in the spread of salmonellae is not known, but transmission might occur in this way through contamination from a number of sources. An outbreak of salmonellosis has been traced to head lettuce contaminated by drippings from frozen chicken (E. K. Borman, personal communication). In an effort to keep the lettuce chilled, the crates were loaded in the bottom of the bed of a truck, and containers of frozen dressed chicken were placed on top. During transportation, some thawing of the chicken took place, and contaminated fluids drained down into the lettuce. This is an excellent example of the need for education at all levels of food handling.

There are a number of reports in the literature on the simultaneous occurrence of two or more serotypes of *Salmonella* in infected individuals, both man and other animals.[27, 45, 171, 178, 181-184] Multiple infections undoubtedly indicate a common source, e.g., multiply infected fowl infecting man.

Two other modes of transmission of salmonellae should be mentioned. First, innocuous foods may be contaminated by utensils previously used to cut or serve contaminated items.[185] Second, adequately cooked food such as chicken or turkey may be recontaminated when it is returned to a previously contaminated area (e.g., a cutting board) for additional preparation.[155]

ANIMAL FEEDS AND FEED INGREDIENTS

In the past it was generally believed that animal feeds were of little importance in the transmission of salmonellae to animals. This notion was based primarily on the observation that serotype Typhimurium, the most commonly occurring *Salmonella* in both lower animals and man, was isolated infrequently from feeds. This discrepancy probably has contributed more than anything else to the fact that positive action has not been taken to control contamination of feeds. Several observations indicate that this discrepancy is more apparent than real.

1. That the methods used for isolating *Salmonella* have a marked effect upon the individual serotypes recovered has been reported.[186] This work dealt with *S. cholerae-suis,* primarily, at least in the case of *S. cholerae-suis;* but the fact remains that there are few objective data on the differential effects of commonly employed methods upon the recovery of individual serotypes when they occur in mixed populations. It is known that not all strains of the various serotypes of *Salmonella* grow equally well on brilliant green agar, the isolation medium most commonly used in the United States for the isolation of salmonellae.[187] The very important observation has been made[188, 189] that plating media labeled with the same name but produced by different firms may yield quite different results. The presence of antimicrobial agents in feeds has a marked influence on the isolation of salmonellae.[190]

2. When graded doses of seven serotypes of *Salmonella* were fed to day-old chicks, the mortality rate among those fed 1 to 10 cells of serotype Typhimurium exceeded that produced by feeding 100 million cells of the other six.[191] Mortality in all chicks fed serotype Typhimurium was 80 percent, which was four times as great as that in chicks fed similar dosages of the serotype that caused the second highest mortality rate. Hence very small numbers of some strains of serotype Typhimurium in

feed may produce fatal salmonellosis. Such small numbers might be difficult to demonstrate, and in most instances of this sort the chicks would not be examined culturally.

3. If sufficiently extensive examinations are made, the percentage of positive isolations of serotype Typhimurium from certain feed ingredients can be increased.[192] When 50 portions of 50 g each from each of a representative sample of bags of fish meal were cultured, serotype Typhimurium was isolated from 27 percent of all bags examined and from 57 percent of all bags that contained salmonellae.[192]

4. Recent work indicates that the same serotypes of *Salmonella* found in animals (and man) *can* be isolated from animal feeds and feed ingredients,[97, 101, 119, 193-211] although the isolation rate of serotype Typhimurium still is reported to be relatively low in most instances (exception: the work cited just above). A correlation between sample size and numbers of salmonellae recovered from meat and bone meal has been demonstrated.[198] A fourfold increase in sample size doubled the percentage of positive results.

There are many published papers that deal with the occurrence of salmonellae in by-products of animal origin used in animal feeds. In one investigation, 43 serotypes of *Salmonella* were recovered from 175 (18 percent) of 980 samples of such by-products from 22 states.[194] In another study,[199] 28 serotypes were recovered from 37 (18.5 percent) of 200 samples of poultry and other animal by-products used in feeds. In a third investigation,[202] 5,712 samples of bone meal, feather meal, tankage, fish meal, egg products, and completed feeds were examined. Of these, 718 (13 percent) contained 59 serotypes. Serotypes Montevideo, Senftenberg, Typhimurium, Cubana, Infantis, and Oranienburg were isolated most frequently.[203] Nine of 16 samples of domestic fish meal from various commercial sources yielded eleven serotypes of *Salmonella*.[204] A single serotype was isolated from only one sample, while two to four serotypes were recovered from each of the other positive specimens. These examples serve to illustrate the importance of animal by-products in the transmission of salmonellae. Numerous other examples are recorded in the references cited.

The role of rendering plants in transmission of salmonellae cannot be overemphasized, since products of these plants are incorporated in animal feeds. Numerous investigations have been made that reveal the presence of *Salmonella* of various serotypes in rendering plants and in the finished products (e.g., References 146, 200, 207, and 211). Further, it would seem that employees of rendering plants might become carriers and transmit infection to members of their families and to the community just as do abattoir workers.[158] This possibility should be investigated. One study of a possibly analogous situation was reported.[212] Adult males who were handling fish meal known to be contaminated with several serotypes of *Salmonella* were asked if they had had diarrhea or vomiting during the preceding month. Of 100 queried, one stated that he had had diarrhea for a day. However, 14 of the men reported that other members of their families had been afflicted with diarrhea and abdominal pain during the same time period.

Similarly, there have been extensive investigations of protein concentrates of vegetable origin incorporated in animal feeds. Salmonellae were isolated in Norway from 42 (4.6 percent) of 910 samples of these products,[196] including cake meals prepared from the following:

32 (16 percent) of 200 samples of cottonseed cake
6 (2.3 percent) of 265 samples of groundnut cake
1 (1 percent) of 84 samples of coconut cake
1 (1 percent) of 91 samples of sunflower seed cake
2 (1 percent) of 200 samples of soybean cake

Serotypes Typhimurium and Derby were isolated from the soybean meal cake and from slaughtered animals that had received it. In Sweden,[197] salmonellae were recovered from a variety of vegetable meal products in addition to those listed above, e.g., rapeseed oil cake. In 1960, salmonellae were recovered from 3.3 percent of 81 samples of oil cake and lucerne meal. Serotypes Oranienburg and Typhimurium were the most commonly occurring salmonellae in these ingredients and in the animals in Sweden.

WATER AND SEWAGE: WATER-BORNE EPIDEMICS OF SALMONELLOSIS

The incidence of typhoid fever has declined in the United States in direct ratio to the number of new waterworks established, the introduction of filtration (about 1906), and the use of chlorination beginning about 1912. However, epidemics of water-borne typhoid fever and gastro-enteritis caused by salmonellae still occur occasionally. This is attested to by the epidemic of typhoid fever that originated in MonArk Springs, Missouri, in 1956, and which was initiated through contamination of well water by a carrier.[213] Another outbreak of typhoid fever occurred in Alaska.[214] In this instance, water was contaminated by droppings from sea gulls that had fed on garbage in sewage effluent discharged into the sea in the area. The water-borne outbreak (1965) of salmonellosis caused by serotype Typhimurium in Riverside, California,[84] illustrates further that transmission by this means still may occur.

During the past 12 years, hundreds of cultures of *Salmonella* isolated by the personnel of many Federal River Basin Projects in various parts of the United States have been examined and characterized (Reference 215 and unpublished data). As might be expected, a variety of serotypes, common to both man and lower animals, were identified. Pollution of rivers affords another mode of transmission of salmonellae to man and other animals. Water supplies of cities and towns downriver from sources of pollution may become contaminated, bathers may become infected, and water fowl may become infected and carry the contamination elsewhere. Contamination of waters by rendering plants and by offal from poultry processing plants has been observed. Flooding of meadows with polluted water has led to contamination of the soil and infection of domestic animals.[216] Cases of salmonellosis in school children arising from school water supply contaminated by sludge from a septic tank have been reported.[217]

The occurrence of salmonellae in irrigation waters and sewage has been reviewed,[217-222] and contamination of coastal bathing waters and river waters has been studied.[223, 224]

Serotypes of *Salmonella* have been isolated from sewage in various stages of treatment, including dried sludge used as fertilizer (unpublished data). A variety of salmonellae have been recovered from organic fertilizers purchased on the open market,[225] and at least the one outbreak of salmonellosis described earlier in this chapter is known in which commercial fertilizer made from dried sludge was the vehicle. The hygienic problems connected with the use and disposal of sewage sludge have been reviewed.[226]

The contamination of shellfish by sewage is well known. As one example of transmission of salmonellae by this means, contamination of shellfish in the area of Long Island may be cited.[227] Several serotypes of *Salmonella* were isolated from discharged wastes flowing from duck farms and from oysters.

The use of contaminated river water to cool canned beef has resulted in at least two epidemics of typhoid fever in the United Kingdom.[228-230] Rapid cooling of the cans caused contaminated water to be pulled into the cans through microleaks. Other salmonellae might contaminate canned products when similar improper processing methods are employed. Canned ham that may have been contaminated in this way[154] was the vehicle of infection in an outbreak of 51 cases of salmonellosis caused by serotype Wien.[231]

MISCELLANEOUS SOURCES AND ROUTES OF INFECTION

Salmonellae have been recovered from a variety of miscellaneous sources, and transmission to man has been reported. It is possible that transmission to lower animals from some of these sources may occur.

Garden soil was the probable source of infection in a family outbreak of gastroenteritis caused by serotype Typhimurium,[232] since the same bacteriophage type was found in garden soil from an area in which the children played and in the patients. The bacteria persisted in the soil for at least 241 days.

Birds other than wild fowl may carry salmonellae. For example, a pet parakeet transmitted infection to a seven-month-old infant.[233] Serotype Typhimurium was isolated from the child and from the bird's droppings. Wild birds such as the house sparrow, starling, and others also may carry salmonellae.[234, 235]

An unusual source of infection in a large outbreak of salmonellosis was whale meat from an infected, ill animal captured by villagers.[236]

An interesting epidemic in a children's ward, which is difficult to categorize but which illustrates several points, was caused by serotype Bovismorbificans.[237] This outbreak was traced to a child six months of age, with bloody diarrhea, admitted to the hospital with a provisional diagnosis of intussusception. This child's father drove a truck used to transport cattle. The same serotype was isolated from the floor of the truck and from the feces of a nine-year-old brother who sometimes rode in the truck.

Serotypes of *Salmonella* have been isolated from a variety of products that are fed to or injected into man and other animals or are used in other ways. These include liver powder and concentrate, thyroid powder and other glandular enzyme preparations such as pancreatin powder, dyes, candy coatings, drugs and dietary substances in tablet or capsule form, vitamin preparations for veterinary use, and enzymatic drain cleaners. One type of drain cleaner deserves special comment. This product, a mixture of lipase, cellulase, and anaerobic and aerobic bacteria, is sold for use in septic tanks, drains, dishwashers, and potato peelers and is used in food-processing plants, creameries, hotels, motels, schools, and the like. The bacteria are said to be nonpathogenic, but eleven 30-g samples from as many containers yielded very large numbers of several serotypes of *Salmonella* (Morris and Thomason, personal communication, 1968). Preliminary examination of the whole product yielded serotypes Cubana, Oranienburg, Senftenberg, Lexington, Infantis, and California. Serotypes California, Senftenberg, Infantis, Lexington, Montevideo, and Cubana were isolated from the lipase constituent, and serotypes Cubana, Lexington, Senftenberg, and Montevideo were recovered from the cellulase. Obviously, products such as this are very dangerous.

To date there has been no reported salmonellosis in the United States attributable to materials that are designed for injection. Such infections have, however, been reported in Sweden.[238]

Carmine dye prepared from dried cochineal insects was the source of infection in 21 cases of salmonellosis in hospitalized patients.[239] Serotype Cubana was easily recovered from the carmine powder, and it was reported that ingestion of as few as 15,000 bacteria was sufficient to produce infection, sometimes fatal, in debilitated persons, infants, and individuals with altered gastrointestinal function. Some patients carried the organism for six to eight months. Serotype Cubana was never isolated from the scale insect in its natural habitat (L. J. Kunz, personal communication, 1967). The isolation of serotype Natal from cochineal in South Africa has been reported.[240] This serotype was recovered from domestic animals, including cats, at about the same time. Carmine dye is used as coloring in cosmetics, foods, drugs, and candy coating.

Several investigators (see, e.g., Reference 241) have pointed out that, in many parts of the world at least, the food habits of both man and domestic animals have changed. The literature on prepared meals and other food products, including frozen foods, is reviewed in references 100, 156, and 241 and the subject need not be pursued here.

Several reviews on the subject of salmonellosis and its control[20, 39, 47, 212, 241-245] agree generally that emphasis should be placed on the necessity for concerted action by governmental agencies concerned with health, agriculture, and foods, and the responsibility is shared by the physician and health officer, the veterinarian and veterinary health officer, and the sanitarian.

Measures long indicated and advocated for control of salmonellosis were reviewed ten years ago.[34] Knowledge sufficient to attack the problem successfully has been available, but it is only within the past few years that enough importance has been attached to the problem of salmonellosis, and enough interest aroused, to implement certain of the long-standing recommendations and to take some first steps toward control. Unfortunate as it may seem, the preliminary measures that have been taken have been dictated as much by economic considerations as by concern for public health. By no means are all manufacturers insensitive to the public health aspects of the problem of salmonellosis; many are, but the fact remains that economic pressures are often effective in achieving desired results.[245]

REFERENCES

1. E. Seligmann, I. Saphra, and M. Wassermann, "*Salmonella* Infections in the U.S.A.," *J. Immunol.*, *54*, 69 (1946).
2. H. Abramson, H. Greenberg, S. Plotkin, and C. Oldenbusch, "Food poisoning in Infants caused by Egg-yolk Powder," *Amer. J. Dis. Child.*, *87*, 1 (1954).
3. I. M. Mackerras and V. M. Pask, "Infant *Salmonella* Carriers," *Lancet, ii*, 940 (1949).
4. G. M. Eisenberg, A. J. Palazzolo, and H. F. Flippin, "Clinical and Microbiologic Aspects of Salmonellosis. A Study of Ninety-five Cases in Adults and Children," *N. Engl. J. Med.*, *253*, 90 (1955).
5. F. S. Leeder, "An Epidemic of *Salmonella panama* Infections in Infants," *Ann. N.Y. Acad. Sci.*, *66*, 54 (1956).
6. V. L. Szanton, "Epidemic Salmonellosis: A 30-month Study of 80 Cases of *Salmonella oranienburg* Infection," *Pediatrics*, *20*, 794 (1957).
7. J. O. Murray and J. H. C. Walker, "An Outbreak of Enteritis (*Salmonella heidelberg*) in a Maternity Unit," *Med. Offic.*, *100*, 221 (1958).
8. J. E. McGuigan, W. C. Berry, and P. R. Carlquist, "Comparison of Chloramphenicol, Oxytetracycline, and Prochlorperazine in *Salmonella* Gastroenteritis," *U.S. Armed Forces Med. J.*, *11*, 1288 (1960).
9. W. E. Mosher, Jr., S. M. Wheeler, H. L. Chant, and A. V. Hardy, "An Outbreak due to *Salmonella typhi murium*," *Pub. Health Rep.*, *56*, 2415 (1941).
10. M. M. Galton and M. S. Quan, "*Salmonella* Isolated in Florida during 1943 with the Combined Enrichment Method of Kauffmann," *Amer. J. Pub. Health*, *34*, 1071 (1944).
11. P. R. Edwards, D. W. Bruner, and A. B. Moran, *The Genus* Salmonella: *Its Occurrence and Distribution in the United States*, Bull. No. 525, Ky. Agr. Exp. Sta., Univ. Ky., Lexington (1948).
12. M. M. Galton and A. V. Hardy, "Studies of Acute Diarrheal Diseases. XXI. Salmonellosis in Florida," *Pub. Health Rep.*, *63*, 847 (1948).
13. O. Felsenfeld and V. M. Young, "A Study of Salmonellosis in North and South America," *Amer. J. Trop. Med.*, *29*, 483 (1949).
14. C. E. McCall, W. E. Sanders, J. R. Boring, P. S. Brachman, and M. Wilkingsson, "Delineation of Chronic Carriers of *Salmonella derby* within an Institution for Incurables," *Antimicrob. Agents Chemother.*, *4*, 717 (1964).
15. C. E. McCall, W. T. Martin, and J. R. Boring, "Efficiency of Cultures of Rectal Swabs and Faecal Specimens in Detecting *Salmonella* Carriers: Correlation with Numbers of *Salmonella* Excreted," *J. Hyg.*, *64*, 261 (1966).
16. A. A. Miller, C. G. M. Nicol, and F. Ramsden, "A Prolonged Infection with *Salmonella bovis-morbificans*," *Mon. Bull. Minn. Health*, *19*, 2 (1960).
17. R. A. MacCready, J. P. Reardon, and I. Saphra, "Salmonellosis in Massachusetts: a Sixteen Year Experience," *N. Engl. J. Med.*, *256*, 1121 (1957).
18. M. M. Galton and A. V. Hardy, "The Distribution of Salmonella Infections in Florida during the Past Decade," *Pub. Health Lab.*, *11*, 88 (1953).
19. G. M. Eisenberg, L. Brodsky, W. Weiss, and H. F. Flippin, "Clinical and Microbiological Aspects of Salmonellosis," *Amer. J. Med. Sci.*, *235*, 497 (1958).
20. W. Savage, "Problems of Salmonella Food-Poisoning," *Brit. Med. J.*, *2*, 317 (1956).

21. W. Schaefer, "Über die dauer Infektiositaet von Salmonellosen," *Zentralbl. Bakteriol. I. Orig., 172,* 272 (1958).

22. I. Saphra and J. W. Winter, "Clinical Manifestations of Salmonellosis in Man," *N. Engl. J. Med., 256,* 1128 (1957).

23. V. Bokkenheuser and N. J. Richardson, "The Bacteriology of the Bantu Food Handler," *S. Afr. Med. J., 33,* 784 (1959).

24. P. R. Edwards and M. M. Galton, "Salmonellosis," in *Advan. Vet. Sci., 11,* 1 (1967).

25. A. D. Rubenstein and R. A. MacCready, "Epidemic *Salmonella newport* Infection in a Metropolitan Area," *N. Engl. J. Med., 248,* 527 (1953).

26. T. M. Floyd, J. R. Baranski, and M. El-Gannani, "Recovery of Human Enteric Pathogens on Meat from Butcher Shops in Cairo, Egypt," *J. Infec. Dis., 92,* 224 (1953).

27. I. Olitsky, A. M. Perri, M. A. Shiffman, and M. Werrin, "Smoked Fish as a Vehicle of Salmonellosis," *Pub. Health Rep., 71,* 773 (1956).

28. G. E. Gayler, R. A. MacCready, J. P. Readon, and B. F. McKernan, "An Outbreak of Salmonellosis Traced to Watermelon," *Pub. Health Rep., 70,* 311 (1955).

29. S. Thomson, "The Numbers of Pathogenic Bacilli in Feces in Intestinal Disease," *J. Hyg., 53,* 217 (1955).

30. T. C. R. George, R. W. S. Harvey, and S. Thomson, "The Measurement of the Duration of Infection in Paratyphoid Fever," *J. Hyg., 51,* 532 (1953).

31. M. Lennox, R. W. S. Harvey, and S. Thomson, "An Outbreak of Food Poisoning due to *S. typhi-murium,* with Observations on the Duration of Infection," *J. Hyg., 52,* 311 (1954).

32. S. Thomson, "The Number of Bacilli Harboured by Enteric Carriers," *J. Hyg., 52,* 67 (1954).

33. P. R. Edwards, "*Salmonella* and Salmonellosis," *Ann. N.Y. Acad. Sci. 66,* 44 (1956).

34. P. R. Edwards, "Salmonellosis: Observations on Incidence and Control," *Ann. N.Y. Acad. Sci., 70,* 598 (1958).

35. P. H. Black, L. J. Kunz, and M. N. Swartz, "Salmonellosis—A Review of Some Unusual Aspects," *N. Engl. J. Med., 262,* 811, 864, 921 (1960).

36. M. M. Galton and J. H. Steele, "Laboratory and Epidemiological Aspects of Foodborne Diseases," *J. Milk Food Technol., 24,* 104 (1961).

37. Report. Working Party, Public Health Laboratory Service, "Salmonellae in Abbatoirs, Butchers' Shops, and Home-Produced Meat, and Their Relation to Human Carriers," *J. Hyg., 62,* 283 (1964).

38. S. Thomson, "Paratyphoid Fever and Bakers' Confectionery," *Mon. Bull. Minn. Health, 12,* 187 (1953).

39. J. Taylor, "*Salmonella* and Salmonellosis," *Roy. Soc. Health J., 80,* 253 (1960).

40. E. J. Bowmer, "The Challenge of Salmonellosis: Major Public Health Problem," *Amer. J. Med. Sci., 247,* 467 (1964).

41. Reibmayr (1918). (Quoted by White, Reference 43.)

42. E. Bumke (1925). (Quoted by White, Reference 43.)

43. P. B. White, "The *Salmonella* Group. A System of Bacteriology," *Med. Res. Counc., 4,* 86 (1929). Her Majesty's Stationery Office, London.

44. T. Klein and R. G. Torrey, "Pulmonary Complications of Paratyphoid Fever, with a Report of Four Cases," *Amer. J. Med. Sci., 159,* 548 (1920).

45. E. Hormaeche, N. L. Surraco, C. A. Pelluffo, and P. L. Aleppo, "Causes of Infantile Summer Diarrhea," *Amer. J. Dis. Child., 66,* 539 (1943).

46. E. Neter, "Observations on the Transmission of Salmonellosis in Man," *Amer. J. Pub. Health, 40,* 929 (1950).

47. W. R. Hinshaw and E. McNeil, "*Salmonella* Infection as a Food Industry Problem," *Advan. Food Res., 3,* 209 (1951).

48. J. G. Bate and B. James, "*Salmonella typhimurium* Infection Dust-Borne in Children's Ward," *Lancet ii,* 713 (1958).

49. F. A. Neva, R. J. Nelson, and M. Finland, "Hospital Outbreak of Infections with *Salmonella newington,*" *N. Engl. J. Med., 244,* 252 (1951).

50. I. Saphra and M. Wassermann, "*Salmonella cholerae suis.* A .Clinical and Epidemiological Evaluation of 329 Infections Identified between 1940 and 1954 in the New York Salmonella Center," *Amer. J. Med. Sci., 228,* 525 (1954).

51. A. Balows, "Unusual *Salmonella* Infections," *J. Ky. Med. Ass., 56,* 770 (1958).

52. F. R. Philbrook, R. A. MacCready, H. V. van Roekel, E. S. Anderson, C. F. Smyser, Jr., F. J. Sanen, and W. M. Groton, "Salmonellosis Spread by a Dietary Supplement of Avian Source," *N. Engl. J. Med., 263,* 713 (1960).

53. J. Taylor, "*Salmonella* Infections in Hospitals," pp. 145–156, in *Infection in Hospitals,* Blackwell. Oxford (1963).

54. M. Melzer, G. Altmann, M. Rakowszcyk, Z. H. Yosipovitch, and B. Barsilai, "Salmonellosis Infections of the Kidney," *J. Urol., 94,* 23 (1965).

55. F. Nordbring, B. Bille, and T. Mellbin, "An Extensive Outbreak of Gastroenteritis Caused by *Salmonella newport,*" *Acta Pathol. Microbiol. Scand., 60,* 131 (1964).

56. I. F. Abroms, W. D. Cochran, L. B. Holmes, E. B. Marsh, and J. W. Moore, "A *Salmonella newport* Outbreak in a Premature Nursery with a One-Year Follow-up," *Pediatrics, 37,* 616 (1966).

57. W. R. Hinshaw, E. McNeil, and T. J. Taylor, "Avian Salmonellosis. Types of *Salmonella* Isolated and Their Relation to Public Health," *Amer. J. Hyg., 40,* 264 (1944).

58. R. H. Greenspan and S. B. Feinberg, "Salmonella Bacteremia; A Case with Military Lung Lesions and Spondylitis," *Radiology, 68,* 860 (1957).

59. E. Gildemeister, 1916. (Quoted by White, Reference 43.)

60. J. G. Hughes and D. S. Carroll, "*Salmonella* Osteomyelitis Complicating Sickle Cell Disease," *Pediatrics, 19,* 184 (1957).

61. A. S. Close, M. B. Smith, M. L. Koch, and E. H. Ellison, "An Analysis of Ten Cases of Salmonella Infection on a General Surgical Service," *AMA Arch. Surg., 80,* 972 (1960).

62. E. W. Hook, C. G. Campbell, H. S. Weems, and G. R. Cooper, "*Salmonella* Osteomyelitis in Patients with Sickle-Cell Anemia," *N. Engl. J. Med., 257,* 403 (1957).

63. J. Watt and E. Carlton, "Studies of the Acute Diarrheal Diseases. XVI. An Outbreak of *Salmonella typhimurium* Infection among Newborn Premature Infants," *Pub. Health Rep., 60,* 734 (1945).

64. E. Seligmann, "Mass Invasion of Salmonellae in a Babies' Ward," *Ann. Pediat., 172,* 406 (1949).

65. J. Watt, M. E. Wegman, O. W. Brown, D. J. Schliessmann, E. Maupin, and E. C. Hemphill, "Salmonellosis in a Premature Nursery Unaccompanied by Diarrheal Disease," *Pediatrics, 22,* 689 (1958).

66. H. C. Epstein, A. Hochwald, and R. Ashe, "*Salmonella* Infections of the Newborn Infant," *J. Pediat., 38,* 723 (1951).
67. N. Datta and R. B. Pridie, "An Outbreak of Infection with *Salmonella typhimurium,* in a General Hospital," *J. Hyg., 58,* 229 (1960).
68. I. M. Mackerras and M. J. Mackerras, "An Epidemic of Infantile Gastro-enteritis in Queensland Caused by *Salmonella bovis-morbificans* (Basenau)," *J. Hyg., 47,* 166 (1949).
69. F. J. Sweeney, Jr., and E. L. Randall, *Clinical and Epidemiological Studies of* Salmonella derby *Infections in a General Hospital,* pp. 130–139, in PHS Publ. No. 1262, U.S. Govt. Printing Office, Washington, D.C. (1965).
70. A. D. Rubenstein and R. N. Fowler, "Salmonellosis of the Newborn with Transmission by Delivery Room Resuscitators," *Amer. J. Pub. Health, 45,* 1109 (1955).
71. B. C. Hobbs, "Public Health Significance of Salmonella Carriers in Livestock and Birds," *J. Appl. Bacteriol., 24,* 340 (1961).
72. P. R. Edwards, D. W. Bruner, and A. B. Moran, "*Salmonella* Infections of Fowls," *Cornell Vet., 38,* 247 (1948).
73. P. R. Edwards, D. W. Bruner, and A. B. Moran, "Further Studies on the Occurrence and Distribution of Salmonella Types in the United States," *J. Infec. Dis., 83,* 220 (1948).
74. D. W. Bruner and A. B. Moran, "*Salmonella* Infection of Domestic Animals," *Cornell Vet., 39,* 53 (1949).
75. C. A. Brandly, "Poultry Diseases as Public Health Problems," *Pub. Health Rep., 66,* 668 (1951).
76. M. M. Galton and A. V. Hardy, "The Distribution of Salmonella Infections in Florida during the Past Decade," *Pub. Health Lab., 11,* 88 (1953).
77. M. M. Galton, D. C. Mackel, A. L. Lewis, W. C. Haire, and A. V. Hardy, "Salmonellosis in Poultry and Poultry Processing Plants in Florida," *Amer. J. Vet. Res., 16,* 132 (1955).
78. A. Buxton, "Salmonellosis in Animals," *Vet. Rec., 70,* 1044 (1958).
79. D. Brobst, J. Greenberg, and H. M. Gezon, "Salmonellosis in Poultry and Poultry Processing Plants in Western Pennsylvania," *J. Amer. Vet. Med. Ass., 133,* 435 (1958).
80. R. F. Gordon, "Broiler Diseases," *Vet Rec., 71,* 994 (1959).
81. J. E. Williams, "Paratyphoid and Paracolon Infections," pp. 202–248, in *Diseases of Poultry,* 4th ed., Iowa State Univ. Press., Ames, Iowa (1959).
82. J. H. C. Walker, "The Broiler Industry—Transmission of Salmonella Infection," *Roy. Soc. Health J., 80,* 142 (1960).
83. Annual Summary, Salmonella Surveillance, 1964, NCDC Publ., Atlanta, Georgia.
84. Annual Summary, Salmonella Surveillance, 1965, NCDC Publ., Atlanta, Georgia.
85. K. D. Quist, "Salmonellosis in Poultry," *Pub. Health Rep., 78,* 1071 (1963).
86. H. van Roekel, "*Salmonella* in Poultry and Eggs," pp. 78–83, in *Proc. Nat. Conf. on Salmonellosis, 1964,* PHS Publ. No. 1262, U.S. Govt. Printing Office, Washington, D.C. (1965).
87. A. S. Anderson, H. Bauer, and C. B. Nelson, "Salmonellosis due to *Salmonella typhimurium* with Easter Chicks as Likely Source," *J. Amer. Med. Ass., 158,* 1153 (1955).
88. J. E. McCroan, T. W. McKinley, A. Brim, and C. H. Ramsey, "Five Salmonellosis Outbreaks Related to Poultry Products," *Pub. Health Rep., 78,* 1073 (1963).

89. A. B. Moran, "Occurrence and Distribution of Salmonella in Animals in United States," *Proc. 65th Ann. Meet. U.S. Livestock Sanit. Ass., Minneapolis, Minn.,* 441 (1962).

90. E. S. Anderson, N. S. Galbraith, and C. E. D. Taylor, "An Outbreak of Human Infection due to Salmonella typhimurium Phage-Type 20a Associated with Infection in Calves," *Lancet, i,* 854 (1961).

91. T. A. Rude, Jr., "*Salmonella typhimurium* Infections in Cattle," *J. Amer. Vet. Med. Ass., 142,* 751 (1963).

92. W. A. Knox, N. S. Galbraith, M. J. Lewis, G. C. Hickie, and H. H. Johnston, "A Milk-borne Outbreak of Food Poisoning due to Salmonella heidelberg," *J. Hyg., 61,* 175 (1963).

93. E. M. Ellis, "Salmonellosis in Florida Cattle," *Proc. 65th Ann. Meet. U.S. Livestock Sanit. Ass., Minneapolis, Minn.,* 161 (1962).

94. G. R. Moore, H. Rothenbacher, M. V. Bennett, and R. D. Barnes, "Bovine Salmonellosis," *J. Amer. Vet. Med. Ass., 141,* 841 (1962).

95. E. T. Davies and J. A. J. Venn, "The Detection of a Bovine Carrier of Salmonella heidelberg," *J. Hyg., 60,* 495 (1962).

96. E. M. Ellis, "Salmonellosis in Cattle, Horses, and Feeds," *Midwest Interprofessional Seminar on Diseases Common to Man and Animals,* Iowa State Univ., Ames (1962).

97. Report, "Salmonellae in Cattle and Their Feedingstuffs, and the Relation to Human Infection," *J. Hyg., 63,* 223 (1965).

98. R. W. Crowther, "*Salmonella* Infection in Sheep in Cyprus," *Vet. Rec., 69,* 695 (1957).

99. G. C. Shearer, "An Outbreak of Abortion in Ewes due to Salmonella dublin," *Vet Rec. 69,* 693 (1957).

100. B. C. Hobbs, "*Salmonella* in Foods," pp. 84–93, in *Proc. Nat. Conf. Salmonellosis, 1964,* PHS Publ. No. 1262, U.S. Govt. Printing Office, Washington, D.C. (1965).

101. R. W. Newell, R. McClarin, and C. R. Murdock, "Salmonellosis in Northern Ireland with Special Reference to Pigs and *Salmonella* Contaminated Pig Meal," *J. Hyg., 57,* 92 (1959).

102. E. Hormaeche and R. Salsamendi, "El Cerdo Normal Como 'Portador' de Salmonelas," *Arch. Med. cir. y espec.* (Montevideo), 14, 375 (1939).

103. M. M. Galton, W. V. Smith, H. B. McElrath, and A. V. Hardy, "*Salmonella* in Swine and Cattle and the Environment of Abattoirs," *J. Infec. Dis., 95,* 236 (1954).

104. L. Leistner, J. Johantges, R. H. Deibel, and C. F. Niven, "The Occurrence and Significance of Salmonellae in Meat Animals and Animal By-product Feeds," *Proc., Amer. Meat Inst. Found. Cong.,* Univ. of Chicago (1962).

105. R. Hansen, R. Rogers, S. Emge, and N. J. Jacobs, "Incidence of Salmonellla in the Hog Colon as Affected by Handling Practices Prior to Slaughter," *J. Amer. Vet. Med. Ass., 145,* 139 (1964).

106. L. P. Williams and K. W. Newell, "Patterns of *Salmonella* Excretion in Market Swine," *Amer. J. Pub. Health, 57,* 466 (1967).

107. M. W. Hale, Personal Communication to Dr. P. R. Edwards (1960).

108. R. V. Lewis, "Salmonellosis in Cattle," pp. 11–18, in *Proc. of Salmonella Seminar,* ARS No. 91–50 Agr. Res. Serv., U.S. Dep. Agr. (1964).

109. F. Kauffman and E. J. Hennigsen, "Über einen neuen Salmonella-Typus bei Mensch und Katze," *Z Hyg. Infek., 120,* 640 (1938).

110. J. Caspersen, "Hund also wahrscheinliche Infektionsquelle eines kleinen Paratyphus-B-Ausbruches," *Z. Hyg. Infek.*, *120*, 611 (1938).
111. S. Gard, "Ein neuer Salmonella-Typ (*S. abortus canis*)," *Z. Hyg. Infek.*, *121*, 139 (1938).
112. E. McNeil and W. R. Hinshaw, "Snakes, Cats, and Flies as Carriers of *Salmonella typhimurium*," *Poult. Sci. 23*, 456 (1944).
113. L. Kintner, "Canine Salmonellosis," *Vet Med.*, *44*, 396 (1949).
114. A. H. Wolff, N. D. Henderson, and G. L. McCallum, "*Salmonella* from Dogs and the Possible Relationship to Salmonellosis in Man," *Amer. J. Pub. Health*, *38*, 403 (1948).
115. M. M. Galton, J. E. Scatterday, and A. V. Hardy, "Salmonellosis in Dogs. I. Bacteriological, Epidemiological and Clinical Considerations," *J. Infec. Dis.*, *91*, 1 (1952).
116. D. C. Mackel, M. M. Galton, H. Gray, and A. V. Hardy, "Salmonellosis in Dogs. IV. Prevalence in Normal Dogs and Their Contacts," *J. Infec. Dis.*, *91*, 15 (1952).
117. C. L. Stucker, M. M. Galton, J. Cowdery, and A. V. Hardy, "Salmonellosis in Dogs. II. Prevalence and Distribution in Greyhounds in Florida," *J. Infec. Dis.*, *91*, 6 (1952).
118. H. B. McElrath, Jr., M. M. Galton, and A. V. Hardy, "Salmonellosis in Dogs. III. Prevalence in Dogs in Veterinary Hospitals, Pounds, and Boarding Kennels," *J. Infec. Dis.*, *91*, 12 (1952).
119. C. A. Griffin, "A Study of Prepared Feeds in Relation to Salmonella Infection in Laboratory Animals," *J. Amer. Vet. Med. Ass.*, *121*, 197 (1952).
120. C. T. Caraway, A. E. Scott, N. C. Roberts, and G. H. Hauser, "Salmonellosis in Sentry Dogs," *J. Amer. Vet. Ass.*, *135*, 599 (1959).
121. P. H. Mann, I. Saphra, and P. B. Hudson, "*Salmonella* Types Found in the Mesenteric Lymph Glands of Dogs and Cats in New York City and Vicinity," *Cornell Vet.*, *43*, 462 (1953).
122. H. Welch, M. Ostrolenk, and M. T. Bartram, "Role of Rats in the Spread of Food Poisoning Bacteria of the *Salmonella* Group," *Amer. J. Pub. Health*, *31*, 332 (1941).
123. G. B. Ludlam, "*Salmonella* in Rats with Special Reference to Findings in a Butcher's By-products Factory," *Mon. Bull. Minn. Health*, *13*, 196 (1954).
124. A. I. Flowers, "Interspecies Transmission of *Salmonella*," pp. 23–29, in *Proc. of Salmonella Seminar*, ARS No. 91-50, Agr. Res. Serv., U.S. Dep. Agr. (1964).
125. J. R. Gorham, D. R. Cordy, and E. R. Quortrup, "*Salmonella* Infections in Mink and Ferrets," *Amer. J. Vet Res.*, *10*, 183 (1949).
126. P. E. Lee and I. M. Mackerras, "*Salmonella* Infections of Australian Native Animals," *Aust. J. Exp. Biol. Med. Sci.*, *33*, 117 (1955).
127. Z. C. Lins, "Ocorrência do Genero *Salmonella* em Animais Silvestres Capturados na Floresta Amazônica," *Ann. Microbiol.*, *12*, 19 (1964).
128. P. D. Klite and M. Kourany, "Isolation of Salmonellae from a Neotropical Bat," *J. Bacteriol.*, *90*, 831 (1965).
129. W. R. Hinshaw and E. McNeil, "Gopher Snakes as Carriers of Salmonellosis and Paracolon Infections," *Cornell Vet.*, *34*, 248 (1944).
130. W. R. Hinshaw and E. McNeil, "*Salmonella* Types Isolated from Snakes," *Amer. J. Vet. Res., 6*, 264 (1945).
131. M. E. M. Thomas, "Enteritis from Tortoises," *Mon. Bull. Minn. Health*, *16*, 29 (1957).

132. L. P. Williams, Jr., and H. L. Helsdon, "Pet Turtles as a Cause of Salmonellosis," *J. Amer. Med. Ass., 192,* 347 (1965).
133. J. C. Torrey, "Numbers and Types of Bacteria Carried by City Flies," *J. Infec. Dis., 10,* 166 (1912).
134. B. Greenberg and A. A. Bornstein, "Fly Dispersion from a Rural Mexican Slaughterhouse," *Amer. J. Trop. Med. Hyg., 13,* 881 (1964).
135. C. R. Eskey, F. M. Prince, and F. B. Fuller, "Double Infection of the Rat Fleas, *X. cheopsis* and *N. fasciatus* with Pasteurella and Salmonella," *Pub. Health Rep., 66,* 1318 (1951).
136. R. Reitler and R. Menzel, "Some Observations on *Salmonella* Strains in Dogs, Mice, and Ticks," *Trans. Roy. Soc. Trop. Med. Hyg., 39,* 523 (1946).
137. P. Y. Liu, S. H. Zia, and H. L. Chung, "*Salmonella enteritidis* Infection by Parenteral Route," *Proc. Soc. Exp. Biol. Med., 37,* 17 (1937-38).
138. Report, Medical Research Council, "Bacteriology of Spray-dried Egg with Particular Reference to Food Poisoning," *Spec. Rep. Ser., 260,* 1, H.M.S.O., London (1947).
139. M. Solowey, V. H. McFarlane, E. H. Spaulding, and C. Chemerda, "Microbiology of Spray-dried Whole Egg. II. Incidence and Types of *Salmonella,*" *Amer. J. Pub. Health, 37,* 971 (1947).
140. J. Watt, "An Outbreak of *Salmonella* Infection in Man from Infected Chicken Eggs," *Pub. Health Rep., 60,* 835 (1945).
141. K. W. Newell, B. C. Hobbs, and E. J. G. Wallace, "Paratyphoid Fever Associated with Chinese Frozen Whole Egg: Outbreaks in Two Bakeries," *Brit. Med. J., 2,* 1296 (1955).
142. S. L. Skoll and H. O. Dillenberg, "*Salmonella thompson* in Cake-mix," *Can. J. Pub. Health, 54,* 325 (1963).
143. F. S. Thatcher, "Health Problems in the Food Industry," *Can. J. Pub. Health, 55,* 151 (1964).
144. F. S. Thatcher and J. Montford, "Egg Products as a Source of Salmonellae in Processed Foods," *Can. J. Pub. Health, 53,* 61 (1962).
145. E. B. Shots, W. T. Martin, and M. M. Galton, "Further Studies on Salmonella in Human and Animal Foods and in the Environment of Food Processing Plants," pp. 309–318, in *Proc. 65th Ann. Meet. U.S. Livestock Sanit. Ass., Minneapolis, Minn.* (1962).
146. M. M. Galton, "*Salmonella* in Miscellaneous Foods," pp. 95–98, in *Proc. Nat. Conf. Salmonellosis,* PHS Publ. No. 1262, U. S. Govt. Printing Office, Washington, D.C. (1965).
147. A. Gärtner, "Über die Fleischvergiftung in Frankenhausen a K. und den erreger Derselben," *Corresp. d. allgemein. ärztl. Vereins. Thuringen, 17,* 573 (1888).
148. F. Basenau, "Über eine im Fleisch gefundene infektiose Bacterie," *Arch. Hyg. 20,* 242 (1894).
149. W. B. Cherry, M. Scherago, and R. H. Weaver, "The Occurrence of *Salmonella* in Retail Meat Products," *Amer. J. Hyg., 37,* 211 (1943).
150. M. M. Galton, W. D. Lowery, and A. V. Hardy, "Salmonella in Fresh and Smoked Pork Sausage," *J. Infec. Dis., 95,* 232 (1954).
151. E. Wilson, R. S. Paffenbarger, Jr., M. J. Foter, and K. H. Lewis, "Prevalence of Salmonellae in Meat and Poultry Products," *J. Infec. Dis., 109,* 166 (1961).

152. J. H. Richardson, M. M. Galton, and L. E. Starr, "Potential Bacterial Pathogens in Retail Market Foods," presented at the Ann. Meet. of the Amer. Vet. Med. Ass., Denver, Colo., August 16, 1960.

153. A. S. Browne, "The Public Health Significance of *Salmonella* on Poultry and Poultry Products," Sum. Diss., Univ. of Calif. N. Sect. (1949).

154. W. W. Sadler, R. Yamamoto, H. E. Adler, and G. F. Stewart, "Survey of Market Poultry for *Salmonella* Infection," *Appl. Microbiol., 9,* 72 (1961).

155. D. C. Mackel, F. J. Payne, and C. I. Pirkle, "Outbreak of Gastroenteritis Caused by *S. typhimurium* Acquired from Turkeys," *Pub. Health Rep., 74,* 746 (1959).

156. F. L. Bryan, J. C. Ayres, and A. A. Kraft, "Salmonellae Associated with Further-processed Turkey Products," *Appl. Microbiol., 16,* 1 (1968).

157. E. de la Cruz, "Epidemiologia de la Salmonelosis en Costa Rica. III. Salmonelas en Manipuladores de Carnes Procesadas," *Rev. de Biol. Trop., Univ. de Costa Rica, 7,* 1 (1959).

158. K. W. Newell, "Methods of Investigating the International Spread of Salmonella," pp. 464–469, in *Proc. 65th Ann. Meet., U.S. Livestock and San. Ass.,* MacCrelish and Quigley, Trenton, N.J. (1962).

159. A. M. McCall, "An Explosive Outbreak of Food Poisoning Caused by *Salmonella dublin,*" Lancet, i, 1302 (1953).

160. R. J. Schroeder and M. B. Dale, "*Salmonella dublin* from Cows Contaminates Market Milk," *J. Amer. Vet. Med. Ass., 136,* 161 (1960).

161. Surveillance Report No. 49, NCDC Publ., Atlanta, Ga. (1966).

162. Surveillance Report No. 57, NCDC Publ., Atlanta, Ga. (1967).

163. R. D. Alley and M. Pijoan, "*Salmonella javiana* Food Infection," *Yale J. Biol. Med., 15,* 229 (1942).

164. C. B. Tucker, G. M. Cameron, M. P. Henderson, and M. R. Beyer, "*Salmonella typhimurium* Food Infection from Colby Cheese," *J. Amer. Med. Ass., 131,* 1119 (1946).

165. F. W. Fabian, "Cheese and Its Relation to Disease," *Amer. J. Pub. Health, 37,* 987 (1947).

166. G. Mocquot, P. Lafont, and L. Vassal, "Nouvelles Observations Concernant la Survie des *Salmonella* dans les Fromages," *Ann. Inst. Pasteur, 104,* 570 (1963).

167. L. J. Kunz and T. G. Ouchterlony, "Salmonellosis Originating in a Hospital. A Newly Recognized Source of Infection," *N. Engl. J. Med., 253,* 761 (1955).

168. C. E. McCall, R. N. Collins, D. B. Jones, A. F. Kaufmann, and P. S. Brachman, "An Interstate Outbreak of Salmonellosis Traced to a Contaminated Food Supplement," *Amer. J. Epidemiol., 84,* 32 (1966).

169. L. Silverstolpe, U. Plazikowski, J. Kjellander, and G. Vahlne, "An Epidemic among Infants Caused by *Salmonella muenchen,*" *J. Appl. Bacteriol., 24,* 134 (1961).

170. J. Kleeman, S. Frant, and A. E. Abrahamson, "Food Poisoning Outbreaks Involving Smoked Fish. Their Epidemiology and Control," *Amer. J. Pub. Health, 32,* 151 (1942).

171. Annual Summary, Salmonella Surveillance for 1966, NCDC Publ., Atlanta, Ga. (1967).

172. E. F. Mackenzie, "Typhoid and Coconut. An Unexpected and Dangerous Combination," *Health Bull., 110,* 19, Melbourne (1953).

173. N. S. Galbraith, B. C. Hobbs, M. E. Smith, and A. J. H. Tomlinson, "*Salmonella* in Desiccated Coconut, an Interim Report," *Mon. Bull. Minn. Health, 19,* 99 (1960).

174. C. I. Wang, "Chinese Soybean Sauce as Transmitting Agent of Bacterial Gastroentestinal Infections," *Amer. J. Trop. Med., 25,* 47 (1945).

175. Surveillance Report No. 22, NCDC Publ., Atlanta, Ga. (1964).

176. V. Glass, G. W. Goodhart, and E. A. Straker, "An Outbreak of Food Poisoning Caused by *Salmonella tyhpi-murium* Conveyed by Infected Gelatin," *Mon. Bull. Minn. Health, 5,* 90 (1946).

177. Surveillance Report No. 61, NCDC Publ., Atlanta, Ga. (1967).

178. M. M. Galton and A. V. Hardy, "Studies of the Acute Diarrheal Diseases. XXI. Salmonellosis in Florida," *Pub. Health Rep., 63,* 847 (1948).

179. A. P. Greenblatt, P. D. Delay, L. Breslow, and I. J. Greenblatt, "*Salmonella* Epidemic from Commercially Prepared Sandwiches," *Bull. U.S. Army Med. Dep., 5,* 345 (1946).

180. J. D. McCluskie, "Vending Machine Salmonellosis," *Morbidity and Mortality Weekly Rep., 11,* 202 (1962).

181. W. L. Mallman, J. F. Ryff, and E. Matthews, "Studies on the *Salmonella* Group—Methods of Isolation and Pathogenicity of Strains Occurring in the Intestines of Chickens," *J. Infec. Dis., 70,* 253 (1942).

182. H. A. Weiner and J. B. Liebler, "Infections with Multiple Salmonella Types, including *S. braenderup,*" *J. Amer. Med. Ass., 145,* 802 (1951).

183. A. P. Juenker, "Infection with Multiple Types of Salmonellae," *Amer. J. Clin. Pathol., 27,* 646 (1957).

184. K. F. Petersen, "Mehrfachinfektionen mit pathogen Darmbakterien," *Z. Hyg., 146,* 13 (1959).

185. L. W. Grogan, "Diseases Transmissable to Man by Food and Food Utensils," *J. Med. Ass., Ala., 17,* 253 (1948).

186. H. W. Smith, "The Evaluation of Culture Media for the Isolation of Salmonellae from Faeces," *J. Hyg., 50,* 21 (1952).

187. W. B. Cherry, B. R. Davis, P. R. Edwards, and R. B. Hogan, "A Simple Procedure for the Identification of the Genus *Salmonella* by Means of a Specific Bacteriophage," *J. Lab. Clin. Med., 44,* 51 (1954).

188. E. H. Kampelmacher, "Salmonellosis in the Netherlands," *Ann. Inst. Pasteur, 104,* 647 (1963).

189. G. K. Morris, "Evaluation of Certain Techniques in Detecting Salmonellae," *Surveillance Rep. No. 74,* NCDC Publ., Atlanta, Ga. (1968).

190. B. S. Pomeroy, p. 101, in *Proc. Nat. Conf. Salmonellosis, 1964,* PHS Publ. No. 1262, U.S. Govt. Printing Office, Washington, D. C. (1965).

191. W. Henderson, J. Ostendorf, and G. L. Morehouse, "The Relative Pathogenicity of Some *Salmonella* Serotypes for Chicks," *Avian Dis., 4,* 103 (1960).

192. J. Jacobs, P. A. M. Guinée, E. H. Kampelmacher, and A. van Keulen, "Studies on the Incidence of *Salmonella* in Imported Fish Meal," *Zentralbl. Veterinarmed., 10,* 542 (1963).

193. C. I. Boyer, Jr., D. W. Bruner, and J A. Brown, "*Salmonella* Organisms Isolated from Poultry Feed," *Avian Dis., 2,* 396 (1958).

194. B. S. Pomeroy and M. K. Grady, "*Salmonella* Organisms Isolated from Feed Ingredients," *Proc. U.S. Livestock Sanit. Ass., 65,* 449 (1961).

195. C. I. Boyer, Jr., S. Narotsky, D. W. Bruner, and J. A. Brown, "Salmonellosis in Turkeys and Chickens Associated with Contaminated Feed," *Avian Dis.*, 6, 43 (1962).

196. S. Hauge and K. Bovre, "The Occurrence of *Salmonella* Bacteria in Imported Vegetable Concentrates and Mixed Concentrates," *Nord. Veterinaermed.*, 10, 225 (1958).

197. K.-A. Karlsson, L. Rutqvist, and E. Thal, "*Salmonella* Isolated from Animals and Animal Feeds in Sweden during 1958–1962," *Nord. Veterinaermed.*, 15, 833 (1963).

198. R. W. S. Harvey, T. H. Price, A. R. Davis, and R. B. Morley-Davies, "An Outbreak of Salmonella Food Poisoning Attributed to Bakers' Confectionery," *J. Hyg.*, 59, 105 (1961).

199. J. R. Watkins, A. I. Flowers, and L. C. Grumbles, "*Salmonella* Organisms in Animal Products Used in Poultry Feeds," *Avian Dis.*, 3, 290 (1959).

200. A. F. Kaufmann and J. C. Feeley, "Culture Survey of Salmonella at a Broiler Raising Plant," *Pub. Health Rep.*, 83, 417 (1968).

201. W. A. Knox, N. S. Galbraith, M. J. Lewis, G. C. Hickie, and H. H. Johnston, "A Milk-borne Outbreak of Food Poisoning due to *Salmonella heidelberg*," *J. Hyg.*, 61, 175 (1963).

202. L. G. Morehouse and E. E. Wedman, "*Salmonella* and Other Disease-producing Organisms in Animal By-products—a Survey," *J. Amer. Vet. Med. Ass.*, 139, 989 (1961).

203. E. E. Wedman, "Findings and Recommendations of the United States Department of Agriculture Task Force on Salmonella in Animal By-products and Feeds," pp. 458–463, in *Proc., 65th annual meeting, U.S. Livestock Sanit. Ass.*, Minneapolis, Minn., October 1961.

204. J. R. Boring, "Domestic Fish Meal as a Source of Various Salmonella Types," *Vet. Med. 53*, 311 (1958).

205. M. M. Galton, J. H. Steele, and K. W. Newell, "Epidemiology of Salmonellosis in the United States," pp. 421–444, in *World Problem of Salmonellosis*, Dr. W. Junk, The Hague, The Netherlands (1964).

206. M. L. Wright, G. W. Anderson, and N. A. Epps, "*Salmonella* Isolations from Feed Additives of Animal Origin," *Can. J. Pub. Health, 53*, 36 (1962).

207. B. S. Pomeroy, Y. Siddiqui, and M. K. Grady, pp. 74–77, in *Proc. Nat. Salmonellosis, 1964, Conf.*, PHS Publ. No. 1262, U.S. Govt. Printing Office, Washington, D.C. (1965).

208. J. D. Clise and E. E. Swecker, "Salmonellae from Animal Byproducts," *Pub. Health Rep., 80*, 899 (1965).

209. R. Angelotti and K. H. Lewis, "Salmonellosis and the Meat Industry," pp. 56–71, in *Proc. Ind. Res. Conf.*, Univ. of Chicago (1966).

210. A. I. Moyle, "Salmonellosis Epidemiology in Wisconsin," pp. 39–40, in *Proc. Salmonella Seminar*, ARS No. 91-50, Agr. Res. Serv., U.S. Dep. Agr., (1964).

211. K. I. Loken, K. H. Culbert, R. E. Solee, and B. S. Pomeroy, "Microbiological Quality of Protein Feed Supplements Produced by Rendering Plants," *Appl. Microbiol., 16*, 1002 (1968).

212. K. W. Newell, "The Investigation and Control of Salmonellosis," *WHO Bull., 21*, 279 (1959).

213. W. A. Neill, J. D. Martin, E. A. Belden, and W. Y. Trotter, "A Widespread Epidemic of Typhoid Fever Traced to a Common Exposure," *N. Engl. J. Med., 259,* 667 (1958).
214. A. N. Wilson and R. Baade, "Salmonellosis Traced to Sea Gulls in Ketchikan," *Alaska Med. 1,* 18 (1959).
215. F. T. Brezenski, R. Russomanno, and P. De Falco, Jr., "The Occurrence of Salmonella and Shigella in Post-chlorinated and Non-chlorinated Sewage Effluents and Receiving Waters," *Health Lab. Sci., 2,* 40 (1965).
216. K. Holtz, "Über die Bedeutung der durch bakteriologische Fleischuntersuchungen ermittelten Salmonellen im Gebeit des Niederrheins," *Arch. Lebensmittelhyg., 7,* 121 (1956).
217. G. A. Dennison, "Contamination of a School Water Supply with Sludge from the Septic Tank," *J. Med. Ass. Ala., 29,* 199 (1959).
218. W. Rudolfs, L. L. Falk, and R. A. Ragotzkie, "Literative Review on the Occurrence and Survival of Enteric, Pathogenic, and Relative Organisms in Soil, Water, Sewage, and Sludges, and on Vegetation. I. Bacterial and Viral Diseases," *Sewage and Ind. Wastes, 22,* 1261 (1950).
219. W. Rudolfs, L. L. Falk, and R. Ragotzkie, "Contamination of Vegetables Grown in Polluted Soil. I. Bacterial Contamination," *Sewage Ind. Wastes, 23,* 253 (1951).
220. S. G. Dunlop, R. M. Twedt, and Wen-Lan-Lou-Wang, "Quantitative Estimation of Salmonella in Irrigation Water," *Sewage Ind. Wastes, 24,* 1015 (1952).
221. N. N. Norman and P. W. Kabler, "Bacteriological Study of Irrigated Vegetables," *Sewage Ind. Wastes, 25,* 605 (1953).
222. Report, 1959, Committee on Bathing Beach Contamination of the Publ. Health Lab. Serv. (B. Moore, Chairman), "Sewage Contamination of Coastal Bathing Waters in England and Wales," *J. Hyg., 57,* 435 (1959).
223. J. H. McCoy, "River Pollution: Bacteriological Aspects and Their Significance," *Roy. Soc. Health J., 83,* 154 (1963).
224. J. H. McCoy, "Salmonellae in Crude Sewage, Sewage Effluent and Sewage-polluted Natural Waters," *Int. Conf. Water Pollut. Res.* (London, Sept. 1962) Pergamon Press, London (1964).
225. J. H. C. Walker, "Organic Fertilizers as a Source of Salmonella Infection," *Lancet, ii,* 283 (1957).
226. A. Speiser, "Hygienic Considerations of Sewage Sludge Utilization," Water Qual. Div., Dep. of Health, Washington, D.C. (1967) (Unpublished).
227. M. H. Bidwell and C. B. Kelly, Jr., "Ducks and Shellfish Contamination," *Amer. J. Pub. Health, 40,* 923 (1950).
228. W. R. M. Couper, K. M. Newell, and D. J. H. Payne, "An Outbreak of Typhoid Fever Associated with Canned Ox-tongue," *Lancet, i,* 1057 (1956).
229. I. Ash, G. D. W. McKendrick, M. H. Robertson, and H. L. Hughes, "Outbreak of Typhoid Fever Connected with Corned Beef," *Brit. Med. J. i,* 1474 (1964).
230. P. M. Lyne and A. J. H. Tomlinson, "Experimental Inoculation of Cans of Corned Beef with *Salmonella typhi,*" *Mon. Bull. Minn. Health, 23,* 147 (1964).
231. J. H. Wildman, C. G. Nicol, and G. H. Tee, "An Outbreak due to *Salmonella wein,*" *Mon. Bull. Minn. Health, 10,* 190 (1951).

232. N. S. Mair and A. I. Ross, "Survival of *Salm. typhi-murium* in the Soil," *Mon. Bull. Minn. Health, 19*, 39 (1960).

233. D. Kaye, H. R. Shinefield, and E. W. Hook, "The Parakeet as a Source of Salmonellosis in Man," *N. Engl. J. Med., 264*, 868 (1961).

234. R. Reitler, "Salmonellosis in Migratory Birds (*Sturnus vulgaris*)," *Proc. VI. Int. Cong. Microbiol., 3*, 253 (1953).

235. C. B. Hudson and D. C. Tudor, "*Salmonella typhimurium* Infection in Feral Birds," *Cornell Vet. 47*, 394 (1957).

236. R. Nakaya, "*Salmonella enteritidis* in a Whale," *Japan Med. J., 3*, 279 (1950).

237. C. H. Jellard, H. Jolly, and R. N. Brown, "An Outbreak of *S. bovis morbificans* Infection in a Children's Ward," *Lancet, i*, 390 (1959).

238. L. O. Kallings, O. Ringertz, and L. Silverstolpe, "Microbiological Contamination of Medical Preparations," *Acta Pharm. Suec., 3*, 219 (1966).

239. D. J. Lang, L. J. Kunz, A. R. Martin, S. A. Schroeder, and L. A. Thomson, "Carmine as a Source of Nosocomial Salmonellosis," *N. Engl. J. Med., 276*, 829 (1967).

240. H. D. Brede, p. 392, in *World Problem of Salmonellosis*. van Oye, ed. Dr. W. Junk, The Hague, The Netherlands (1964).

241. Food Protection Committee, Food and Nutrition Board, *An Evaluation of Public Health Hazards from Microbiological Contamination of Foods*, NAS-NRC Publ. 1195, Natl. Acad. Sci.–Natl. Res. Council, Washington, D.C. (1964).

242. J. Grant, "Salmonellosis," *Med. Offic., 84*, 5, 19 (1950).

243. W. C. Cockburn, "Food Poisoning. (a) Reporting and Incidence of Food Poisoning," *Roy Soc. Health J., 80*, 249 (1960).

244. J. Taylor, "Modern Life and Salmonellosis," *Proc. Roy. Soc. Med., 58*, 167 (1965).

245. P. R. Edwards, "Observations on the Epidemiology of Salmonellosis," in *Proc. 16th Res. Conf., Res. Counc. Amer. Meat Inst. Found.*, Univ. of Chicago (1964).

III

HOW MAN CAN BE PROTECTED

7 Control of Salmonellosis in Animals

Salmonellae inhabit most species of warm-blooded and many cold-blooded vertebrates. Food-producing animals (fowl, cattle, swine, sheep, goats, horses) are commonly infected. Companion pets (dogs, cats) and other household pets (pet birds, turtles) are likewise carriers of salmonellae. The true incidence of salmonellosis in animals is not known. With the exception of pullorum disease and fowl typhoid, salmonella infections of animals are not reportable diseases in most states, and there are 13 states that do not even require that these diseases be reported. The isolations of salmonellae from animals that have been reported in Salmonella Surveillance Reports reflect the activities and interest of the state veterinary diagnostic laboratories and individual research interest.

Salmonellosis may express itself in animals as a clinical disease, particularly in young animals (calves, piglets, lambs, baby chicks, poults, ducklings, and goslings), and in isolated instances results in substantial losses.

In baby chicks and poults, serotypes Typhimurium and Heidelberg infections may cause losses from death as high as 50 to 75 percent. However, under field conditions the average loss lies between 5 and 10 percent. The true status of salmonella infections in poultry is obscured by medications that are commonly used in starter feeds or drinking water. The disease is often inapparent, the animals showing no symptoms and the salmonellae continuing to cycle in the animal population indefinitely because of the contaminated environment.

99

The Animal Health Division, USDA (1967) reported the identification of 56 serotypes from chickens, 49 serotypes from turkeys, 35 from swine, 25 from cattle, 8 from sheep and goats, and 10 from horses.[1] Numerous reports have indicated that animal feeds are contaminated with salmonellae and provide an excellent means of introducing salmonellae into animal and poultry populations. The recent State/Federal Cooperative Survey (1966) covering 26 states substantiated earlier studies that showed animal by-products to be the most heavily contaminated: meat and bone meal, 32 percent; fish meal, 4.7 percent; oilseed meals, 2.3 percent; grains, 0.66 percent; complete poultry feed, 5.32 percent; swine feed, 3.22 percent; and cattle feed, 0.88 percent. Approximately 40 percent of the feed mills tested had salmonella-contaminated products. Sixty different serotypes of *Salmonella* were isolated. A preliminary report of the State/Federal Cooperative Survey of Rendering Plants (USDA, 1967) covering the same 26 states indicated that over 50 percent of the plants were producing salmonella-contaminated products.[2]

The incidence of salmonellae in animals and poultry at the processing plant level is correlated with environmental conditions and feeding practices at the producer and marketing levels. Swine, turkeys, and chickens have higher salmonellae incidence than do cattle and sheep. The facts that they are continuously exposed to salmonella-contaminated feeds and produced under density rearing practices that encourage the cycling of salmonellae in the environment account for the higher incidence. The concentration of cattle and sheep in feed lots encourages the cycling of salmonellae in the animal population and increases the incidence of clinical cases.

In order to recognize ways to reduce salmonellae in food-producing animals and in companion animals and other pets with the ultimate goal of elimination, it is desirable first to review briefly the cycles of salmonella infection in the specific animal hosts.

SALMONELLA CYCLES IN SPECIFIC ANIMAL HOSTS

SALMONELLA CYCLE AT PRODUCER LEVEL

Poultry (chickens, turkeys, ducks, geese)

There are at least two salmonella cycles in poultry.[3]

Egg Transmission   This cycle involves the breeding flock with transmission of salmonellae in or on the surface of the egg (Figure 9). It has

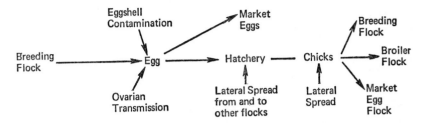

FIGURE 9   Transmission routes in poultry.

long been recognized that host-adapted strains (serotypes Pullorum and Gallinarum) are ovarian transmitted. Certain of the unadapted serotypes (Typhimurium and Heidelberg) have been studied in closed poultry breeding operations. In this case ovarian transmission occurs infrequently, but adult carriers are occasionally encountered as intermittent intestinal shedders, infection persisting in a flock for months. Persistence may in part result from repeated reinfection of the population from a contaminated environment. Chicks, poults, and ducklings for replacement breeder flocks may become exposed at time of hatching or during the brooding and growing periods. They may continue the salmonella cycles as a primary or multiplier flock.

Environmental Cycle   Salmonella-free chicks may be placed in environmental conditions that permit the introduction of salmonellae into the population or in an environment already contaminated. Salmonellae will live for weeks or months in litter, soil, dust, water, and excreta. The common sources of salmonellae are (Figure 10):

- Feed
- Building (floor, walls, ceiling, ventilation equipment) contaminated from previous use
- Free-flying birds (sparrows, pigeons)
- Other animal hosts (dogs, cats, rodents, wildlife)
- Flies, beetles, and other insects
- Water
- Cold-blooded animals (snakes, lizards)
- Airborne (dust)
- Fomites (poultry equipment)
- Man: (a) clothing, footwear; (b) carrier–excreta

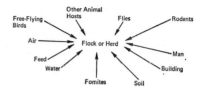

FIGURE 10   Sources of salmonellae at producer level.

In recent years serotype Heidelberg has been isolated from chicken and turkey flocks in many states. It was the serotype most commonly isolated from turkeys and chickens in 1967. Serotype Heidelberg became established in some breeding flocks of chickens and turkeys a few years ago. Salmonella serotypes other than Pullorum and Gallinarum are not subject to mandatory control procedures under the National Poultry Improvement Plan. Typhimurium, Heidelberg, and other serotypes have become widely disseminated in the United States because of present-day practices in the poultry industry. In most states salmonella infections other than pullorum disease and fowl typhoid are not reportable. Salmonella-infected flocks may be used as breeding flocks, and hatching eggs from these flocks may be distributed throughout the United States. There are no federal interstate health regulations governing shipment of live poultry and hatching eggs.

A recent example of the introduction of serotype Typhimurium into a primary turkey breeding flock illustrates the importance of environmental factors and how the infection may mushroom from a single source. In this case a breeder operation had been extensively monitored for three previous years with no isolations of serotype Typhimurium; yet this serotype was recognized in a potential breeder flock at the time of testing under the National Turkey Improvement Plan (NTIP) program. Two other flocks approximately of the same size and age on the same farm were found to be negative. Investigations indicated that the infected flock had recently been transferred into a turkey building that was occasionally used for standby flocks. This building was not secure against free-flying birds, and rodent control was poor in contrast to that practiced in the other buildings on the farm. It so happened that environmental samples (litter, soil, dust) had been taken from this building as well as from the other two buildings on the farm just prior to placing birds in the buildings. Serotype Typhimurium was isolated from the environmental samples from this one building and not from the other two buildings. Two weeks after the birds were placed in the building they were tested with Salmonella antigens and some were found to react to serotype Typhimurium antigen. Serotype Typhimurium was isolated from the reactors submitted for bacteriological tests. The owner was advised to eliminate the flock but chose to qualify the flock by an alternate procedure under the NTIP by which the flock was retested until no reactors were found. Two months later this flock was transferred to laying quarters on another farm that had flocks in production in other buildings. After transfer to the new quarters, shedders were disclosed by fecal swabs, but the flock, upon sample testing, remained serologically negative. The other flocks on this farm were being monitored by sample blood testing and bacteriological examination of fecal swabs and were negative for serotype Typhimurium. It was customary on this farm to move flocks from one building to another to control broodiness. The flock suspected of being infected with serotype Typhimurium was not involved in the flock rotation program, but half of the building in which this flock was housed was used for this program. Within several weeks serotype Typhimurium became established in all the buildings on the farm and all flocks contained shedders. Serotype Typhimurium was recovered from poults from three hatches: one hatch had 13 percent mortality of 15,000 poults, another had 60 percent mortality of 22,000 poults. Future breeder replacement flocks involving 28,000 birds became infected and were marketed. The brooder buildings where all replacement flocks started became contaminated. As a last resort, all turkeys were removed from the two contaminated farms and the buildings cleaned and disinfected. The estimated total cost of this episode was $35,000.

Swine

Salmonellae in pigs may derive from the infected sow, the feed, and the environment.[4] There is but one adapted serotype in swine, *S. choleraesuis*. The unadapted serotypes commonly found in poultry are also isolated from swine.

Animal Cycle   This cycle involves elimination of salmonellae in the excreta of infected breeding stock, resulting in contamination of the environment and infection of piglets early in life. The young pigs may continue to harbor the organisms throughout the growing period. Those that remain in the herd as breeding stock thus complete the cycle and start a new cycle by contaminating the environment.

Environmental Cycle   Salmonella-free swine may be placed in environmental conditions that promote introduction of salmonellae into the population.

The sources of salmonellae for swine are similar to those for poultry. (See Figure 10.)

Cattle

Sources of salmonellae in cattle include the infected adult cow, the feed, and the environment.[5, 6] The two serotypes most frequently isolated from cattle are Dublin and Typhimurium. Serotype Dublin is relatively host-adapted in cattle.

Animal Cycle   This cycle involves elimination of salmonellae in excreta of infected breeding stock, contaminating pen, milk, feeding equipment, etc. and resulting infection of the calf. Calves that are grown to maturity and retained in the herd as breeding stock thus complete the cycle and start a new one.

Environmental Cycle   Salmonella-free swine may be placed in environ-the environment. The pollution of streams, lakes, farm ponds, and other water supplies with salmonellae has been recognized as being associated with outbreaks in cattle.[5]

TRANSPORTATION TO MARKET

Poultry

The present system of marketing broilers, turkeys, and adult fowl usually avoids holding birds at the processing plant for additional fattening and conditioning periods. However, produce trucks and crates may readily become contaminated with salmonellae, and excreta may contaminate the external surface of the transported poultry. Live birds, contaminated internally as well as externally, serve as a means of introducing salmonellae into poultry processing plants.[7, 8]

Swine

Pigs already infected on farms may excrete salmonellae during and after transport.[9] Holding pens at local livestock markets and terminal markets become contaminated and allow spread from pig to pig within a lot or for indirect transfer from other pigs or other sources such as water, feed, or contaminated pens. Transportation vehicles may become contaminated and serve as a source of further spread unless cleaned and sanitized between uses.

Cattle

Calves and feeder and adult cattle may excrete salmonellae during and after the stress of transport. Holding pens at local markets, terminal markets, and stockyards become contaminated and further spread of salmonellae from contaminated pens, water, and feed occurs.

Grau and Brownlie[10] found that 45 percent of the samples of rumen fluid from cattle at slaughter contained salmonellae. In a recent study,

Grau et al.[11] reported high incidence of salmonellae in railcars, saleyards, and holding pens, indicating that cattle were continually exposed during transit from farm to slaughter. An increase in the period between leaving the farm and slaughter increased the percentage incidence of salmonellae in the rumen. Grau et al.[11] also found that feeding cattle in abattoir holding pens after starvation produced a significant increase in the percentage of animals with salmonellae in the rumen or in the feces and in the number of salmonellae in the rumen.

REDUCTION OF SALMONELLA INFECTION IN POULTRY AND LIVESTOCK

An understanding of the cycles of salmonella infection in poultry and livestock points to the means of reducing the incidence of infection at the levels of production and marketing. There are some recommended actions that apply generally. They are:

● Minimize salmonella contamination of animal, poultry, and fish by-products intended for animal feed.
● Extend the effort to all feed ingredients and blended feeds.
● Require that all laboratory-diagnosed salmonella infections be made reportable diseases in all states, and investigate all reported outbreaks.
● Emphasize the need for improving feeding and management programs at the producer level, e.g., control of free-flying birds, rodents, and other pests; provide potable water (Figure 10).

Actions recommended to reduce infections are outlined in greater detail specifically for poultry and the various classes of livestock for application at the producer and market levels.

PRODUCER LEVEL

Poultry

(a) Develop on eradication program for pullorum disease and fowl typhoid involving all chicken and turkey breeding flocks in the United States.

(b) Tailor a salmonella-control program for each primary breeder and multiplier, concentrating on the prevalent serotypes, e.g., Typhimurium and Heidelberg.

(c) Design poultry buildings and equipment so they can be easily cleaned and sanitized.

(d) Develop a total salmonella-control program for chicken and turkey flocks.

Swine

(a) Improve husbandry practices including use of concrete slabs for feeding and pen sanitation.

(b) Design swine buildings and equipment so they can be easily cleaned and sanitized.

(c) Develop breeding herds free of salmonellae and other specific pathogens.

Cattle

Calves (a) Improve husbandry practices to break the salmonella chain from adult to calf. (b) Design dairy and beef cattle buildings and equipment so they can be easily cleaned and sanitized.

Feeder Cattle (a) Improve husbandry practices to minimize soil and water as vehicles of salmonellae infection. (b) Design holding pens and equipment so they can be easily cleaned and sanitized.

Breeding Stock (a) Avoid introduction of infection into the breeding herd by carrier animals. (b) Minimize stresses that favor shedding of salmonellae. (c) Design buildings and equipment so they can be easily cleaned and sanitized. (d) Develop breeding herds that are free of salmonellae and of other bovine diseases.

MARKET LEVEL (PRIOR TO SLAUGHTER)

Poultry

Transportation vehicles and holding crates must be so designed that they can be easily and effectively cleaned and sanitized between uses. Until salmonellae-free poultry are available at the producer level, efforts at control during transport will minimize cross-infection.

Swine

(a) Transportation vehicles must be designed so they can be cleaned and disinfected between uses.

(b) Holding pens at local markets should be so constructed that they can be easily cleaned and disinfected. Salmonella contamination of sources of feed and water should be minimized.

(c) Holding pens at terminal markets should be so designed that they can be readily cleaned and sanitized and maintained as uncontaminated.

(d) Salmonella contamination of sources of feed and water should be minimized.

(e) Free-flying birds, rodents, flies, and other pests at terminal markets should be kept at a minimum.

Cattle

(a) Transportation vehicles must be designed so they can be cleaned and disinfected between uses.

(b) Holding pens should be clean, dry, and uncontaminated.

(c) Salmonella contamination of sources of feed and water should be minimized.

REFERENCES

1. Salmonella Surveillance Report, Annual Summary, NCDC Publ., Atlanta, Georgia (1967).
2. Joseph N. Allred, J. W. Walker, V. C. Beal, Jr., and F. W. Germaine, "A Survey to Determine the Salmonella Contamination Rate in Livestock and Poultry Feeds," *J. Amer. Vet Med. Ass. 151,* 1857 (1967).
3. J. E. Williams, "Paratyphoid and Arizona Infection," p. 260 in Biester and Schwarte, *Diseases of Poultry,* 5th ed., Iowa State Univ. Press, Ames, Iowa (1965).
4. L. P. Williams, Jr., and K. W. Newell, "Sources of Salmonellas in Market Swine," *J. Hyg., 66,* 281 (1968).
5. E. A. Gibson, "Diseases of Dairy Cattle. Salmonella Infection in Cattle," *J. Dairy Res., 32,* 97 (1965).
6. R. V. Lewis, "Salmonellosis in Cattle," Proc. Salmonella Seminar, Hyattsville, Md. *ARS Publ., 91,* 11 (1964).
7. W. W. Sadler, R. Yamamoto, H. E. Adler, and G. F. Stewart, "Survey of Market Poultry for Salmonella Infection," *Appl. Microbiol., 9,* 72 (1961).
8. F. L. Bryan, J. C. Ayres, and A. A. Kraft, "Salmonellae Associated with Further-Processed Turkey Products," *Appl. Microbiol., 16,* 1 (1968).
9. L. P. Williams, Jr., and K. W. Newell, "Patterns of Salmonella Excretion in Market Swine," *Amer. J. Pub. Health, 57,* 466 (1967).
10. F. H. Grau and L. E. Brownlie, "Occurrence of Salmonellas in the Bovine Rumen," *Aust. Vet. J., 41,* 321 (1965).
11. F. H. Grau, L. E. Brownlie, and E. A. Roberts, "Effect of Some Preslaughter Treatments on the Salmonella Population in Bovine Rumen and Faeces," *J. Appl. Bacteriol., 31,* 157 (1968).

8 Control of Contamination in Food Processing

Effective, workable controls in food processing require understanding and cooperation among sanitarians, regulatory agencies, and food processors. There must be no compromise in safeguarding consumer safety, but, on the other hand, setting unrealistic regulatory standards will destroy mutual confidence and respect. Industry must recognize that to demand positive proof of consumer hazard before instituting control is unreasonable and if acceded to would place both industry and regulatory agency in an untenable position. On the other hand, to base controls on zero tolerances, with absolute assurance that under no circumstances would any hazard exist, is unrealistic. It is therefore important to reach an understanding as to what improvements are required to minimize consumer risk and to cooperate in continuing application of improved procedures. Quality control in industry recognizes that safety must be built into the product and testing the finished product actually assists in measuring the effectiveness of process controls. But finished product standards frequently serve as the means of regulatory control and as such may become so involved and costly that economic considerations cause relaxation of the "in-line" controls designed to build the desired safety. Resolution of conflicting concepts would encourage better understanding and cooperation among all involved in food sanitation.

The significance of the phrase "minimize the risk" must be recognized and appreciated. On the basis of present knowledge, one can not guarantee that products that are not terminally treated will be free from salmonellae. Sufficient data have been collected, however, to justify the statement that under good operating conditions the probability of isolation of salmonellae from the finished product in question is low. Information on sanitation controls has been presented in industry and regulatory meetings and is available in published form.[1-7] It is important that this information reach all branches of the food industry and penetrate to the small, local producer as well as to the major operators.

Because of the wide diversity of food products, processing procedures, preservation methods, packaging materials, and distribution methods, special sanitation practices must be designed to cover the individual needs of the industries. It must be recognized that food composition, water activity, pH, osmotic pressure, preservation methods, preservatives, and other factors influence the extent of consumer hazard. There are, however, certain general principles that apply.

INCOMING MATERIAL

Certain incoming materials can be considered by the processor as potentially contaminated. Some examples are carcasses coming to rendering plants, poultry, animals coming to slaughtering establishments, and eggs. In these cases, certification of freedom from, or laboratory testing for, salmonellae and environmental sampling in the raw-materials handling area are of little use. Controls to prevent spread from the raw materials area throughout processing areas and control of processing procedures must be such as to give assurance of the safety of the finished product. It is important to recognize that personnel working in the raw materials area may risk infection and thus should be given training in sanitary practices to minimize that risk.

In many operations, ingredients or materials can be obtained that present a minimum risk of salmonella contamination. In this case, specifications should require that lots be free from salmonellae as measured by the recommended testing procedure. Where past experience indicates potential hazard, lots should be tested and not used in processing until cleared. Certification by the supplier does not assure satisfactory material, but it does force recognition of his responsibility.

Storage areas for incoming materials should be separated from processing and finished product areas. Storage should be so controlled that a product requiring testing will not be utilized until clearance is given. The control requirements are of the utmost importance where the formulated product is not subjected to processing that will destroy salmonellae.

PLANT LOCATION AND LAYOUT

In new construction, processing plants should be located to permit control of the outer perimeters. Control of pests and airborne contamination and sufficient space for proper layout are essential. Processing plants already in operation must function in their existing situations. In such cases the sanitarian must survey the outer perimeter and recommend those controls that will minimize contamination hazards.

In plant layout, the segregation of raw storage and raw processing areas from the processing and storage areas for the finished product is essential. Attention should be given to segregation of operations and personnel within the plant. Toilets should be located to minimize traffic through finished-product areas. It is essential to prevent air flow from potentially contaminated locations to those considered free from contamination. False ceilings, space between walls, ledges, or dust-collecting surfaces increase the difficulty of control. All internal installations should be planned to permit ready access for ease of cleaning. Walls and floors should be readily cleanable.

EQUIPMENT

Equipment is frequently engineered for a particular operation without proper consideration to ease of cleaning and sanitation. Attention to construction permitting access for removal of product and adequate sanitation would assist in production control. Information on a number of types of equipment can be found in the 3A Sanitary Standards.[8] Although the emphasis here is largely on dairy equipment, much of the information is helpful in other food processes. Assistance by health and regulatory authorities prior to installation can avoid the need for possible costly changes.

PASTEURIZATION AND COOLING

Chapter 9 presents information on the lethal effect of heat. Salmonellae are not unusually resistant to heat, and prescribed pasteurization times and temperatures are considered adequate to kill the organism. The important point is that the process be so controlled that the proper temperature and time are assured for the entire product. Deviations from the specified conditions can result in serious errors. Food processors must recognize that the times and temperatures recommended for one type of food product do not apply to all products. The composition, moisture content, and fat content greatly influence conditions required for effective pasteurization.

Prompt and adequate cooling of perishable food products is essential to prevent growth of surviving microorganisms. In cases in which pasteurization is marginal (e.g., eggs), this factor becomes extremely important. Surviving salmonellae may reproduce and result in excessive product contamination.

CLEANING

Proper cleaning procedures, based on knowledge of the process and observation of cleaned equipment, should be developed, understood, and routinely carried out by plant personnel. Training and supervision of individuals to assure continued adherence to the procedures are advisable. An adequate supply of hot and cold water is essential. In the case of hand cleaning, a temperature of 105–120°F (40–49°C) is satisfactory. For "in-place" cleaning, higher temperatures of 140–170°F (60–76°C) should be used. Advice on proper cleansers, procedures, and temperatures can be secured from companies specializing in this field.

Difficulties may be encountered in cleaning dry areas, and caution must be exercised to prevent wetting locations where moisture can be deleterious to the product. The dry areas must be adequately cleaned to prevent accumulation of product or dust. In addition, high humidity, steam, or moist conditions must be prevented.

There are certain suggestions that may be useful but are not covered in the general suggestions. These are:

● Clean equipment used on raw materials in an area separate from that used for processing equipment.

● Routing of cleaning personnel from raw-materials areas to areas in which final processing takes place may result in contamination of clean areas.

● Do not route equipment used in raw-materials areas through areas in which final processing is done.

● Use potable or chlorinated water for both cleaning and rinsing.

● Schedule janitorial work so that janitors are not routed from lavatories to processing areas.

● Store cleaned equipment so it will dry promptly and be protected from contamination.

SANITIZING

Equipment requiring wet cleaning should be properly sanitized prior to the start of operations. Sanitization should follow proper cleaning and is a distinct operation. Adequate duration of contact and concentration of the sanitizing material are essential. Use an approved sanitizer, and follow the instructions on the label to ensure proper concentration.

Quantitative bacteriological studies are a good measure of cleaning and sanitization.

RECONTAMINATION—AIRBORNE

Salmonellae may be carried on dust or in dried product. The processor must realize that accumulations of product, even though initially wet, may when dry result in sources of airborne contamination. Certain processing operations such as separation and comminution may develop extremely finely divided material that can remain suspended in the air.

In processing operations such as dehydration the required air supply may carry salmonellae into the product. For this reason it is important to locate air inlets to minimize pickup of dust or foreign matter. If a neighboring industry handles products that may contribute a salmonella risk, inlets should be located away from this installation. Inlets should not be located near ground level, where dust may be a problem, or where there is risk of drawing in exhaust products from outlet ducts.

Adequate filters should be installed on all inlets. Information on air filtration can be secured from the manufacturers or from published sources.[9] Generally, a low-density filter is installed in the intake line followed by a high-density filter. The low-density material removes larger particles from the air stream and the high-density filter catches finer material. Regular change of filters at air inlet areas will increase the effectiveness of operation and improve processing sanitation. Filtration of air designed for both hot and cold processing is necessary. In hot processing, air is drawn into the system to bring up the temperature, and at present there is no assurance that such air is sterilized by the heating units.

Air circulation within the plant may carry organisms from contaminated to clean areas, and in air-conditioned buildings or areas this often occurs. Where dry cleaning is required, there is danger of airborne contamination, especially if vacuum cleaners expel air into the plant. Portable vacuum cleaners may spread contamination into processing areas; it is preferable to use stationary cleaners that utilize a duct system and expel the discharged air where the hazard of product contamination is minimal.

RECONTAMINATION—FLOOR DRAINS

Considerable evidence has accumulated showing that improperly trapped floor drains are a potential source of environmental contamination. In addition to providing adequate drain traps, floor outlets should be clean and treated at least weekly with a germicidal agent. If drains back up, thorough cleaning and decontamination of the flooded area are essential. It may appear that if such drains are connected to storm sewers they are not important, but one must remember that product from either cleaning operations or other sources may be flushed down these drains. Conditions there are conducive to bacterial growth, and thus heavy contamination of drain outlets and pipes may result.

In designing the drainage system, a separate system should be provided for handling toilet waste. Drains from areas considered highly vulnerable to contamination should be so installed that "backup" cannot contaminate "clean" areas.

WATER SUPPLIES

All water utilized in the food plants should be of safe and sanitary quality and if necessary should be chlorinated. Some processors require chlorination at the plant even though the water is judged safe for drinking. Utilization of contaminated water, without chlorination, for condensers, cooling systems, cleaning, and the like will result in environmental contamination and may lead to product contamination.

In cleaning floors and large pieces of equipment, contaminated water can deposit salmonellae throughout the area, and careless use of hoses can cause dissemination of material into areas from which subsequent removal is difficult. This wet material becomes a potential growth medium and focus of contamination.

PERSONNEL

One problem faced by production management is to prevent contamination of product by personnel who are carriers of salmonellae. The following control measures are suggested:

● Train personnel in sanitary practices, and by proper supervision see that the recommendations are followed. Films and information on proper sanitary practices are available for training.[10] Schedule additional training sessions to assure that personnel recognize and utilize good sanitary practices.

● Insist that personnel with diarrhea so inform management, and reassign them to an area where they will not be in contact with the food product.

● Maintain records of absenteeism that include symptoms of illness. If diarrhea is involved, it is advisable to examine that employee before he returns to work to assure that he is not a salmonella carrier.

● In case of general family illness, information that includes the cause of illness should be secured, and if salmonellae are involved, the employee should not be assigned to a finished-product area until recovery of all family members is complete.

It is essential that supervisory personnel be adequately informed on control programs, the importance of control, and their responsibility for seeing that it is carried out. They must understand that their conduct and support can greatly influence the thinking and behavior of the personnel under their direction. All branches of management must know the regulations of the processing plant and carefully adhere to these rules when their duties require their presence in the processing area. All control programs must have management support and understanding and must be adhered to by management.

Inspection or control personnel may themselves cause spread of contamination as their duties necessitate travel between potentially hazardous and clean areas. If possible, they should be routed first through the clean area and then to the raw-product area. Where this is not possible, controls should be established to minimize the risk of spreading contamination through the plant. These individuals require special training in over-all sanitation and control.

Maintenance personnel constitute a major control problem. When breakdown occurs in a processing operation, prompt corrective action is required, and maintenance men are sometimes moved from a contaminated area to a finished-product line. When this happens, rules of sanitary practice have been ignored, and the line becomes contaminated, particularly if the equipment is placed in operation as soon as repair or corrective action is completed.

The danger of contamination of hands has been stressed for years. Rest rooms in food plants regularly contain signs requiring that hands be washed before returning to work. Unfortunately, many persons consider a quick rinse adequate. Hence, proper instructions for hand washing should be a part of the program. Requirements for hand decontamination are becoming mandatory. Hand washing and decontamination stations must be located throughout the plant to permit easy access and use. Sanitary soap dispensers, as well as dispensers for decontaminating solutions, are advised. Single-service towels and an adequate supply of hot and cold running water should be provided.

The hourly personnel must be instructed in proper operational practices, and their work areas should be limited, to minimize risk of contamination. Exchange of hourly personnel from raw-product areas to finished-product areas is hazardous.

Proper training of personnel and adequate equipment can prevent many incidents of contamination. It must be stressed that equipment utilized in areas considered as potentially contaminated should not be used in areas considered clean. Management must realize the importance of a continuing training program to assure recognition of the importance of sanitary practices.

Many food-processing plants are asked to permit visitors to tour their operations. Because it is difficult to impose regulations on these visitors, such tours should be discouraged.

Valuable information for personnel in food production can be obtained from training programs offered by the Food and Drug Administration.

INSECT AND RODENT CONTROL

Pest control may be carried out by operational personnel or may be handled by a contractor, a portion of the task being assigned to operational personnel. It is essential that there be no areas harboring insects or rodents. Construction must be designed to prevent free access of pests, and the outer perimeter should not encourage infestation. If rodent problems have been encountered, all fecal pellets should be removed, since they may contain salmonella and serve as a focus of contamination.

BIRDS

Because the presence of birds in any area of the building can lead to product contamination, construction and operation must be designed to prevent their entrance.

MICROBIOLOGICAL LABORATORIES

In assuring the effectiveness of salmonella control, laboratory tests are important. Samples may be taken at the processing plant and shipped to a central laboratory under corporate control, or they may be examined by a contract laboratory. If a contract laboratory is utilized, one must be sure that its facilities and personnel are adequate. An inadequate test giving false results can mean either destruction of good product or shipment of contaminated product.

If corporate laboratories are used adequate facilities and competent personnel must be provided, and contamination of the processing areas prevented. Before deciding on testing procedures, advice should be secured from knowledgeable personnel. Suggestions for design of laboratories and for good laboratory practice have been outlined by Hall and Borker,[11] and training programs are available from the National Communicable Disease Center, the Center for Urban and Industrial Health, and The Food Research Institute, University of Wisconsin.

FINISHED PRODUCT

In some processing procedures, in which all or a portion of the product is collected in containers for finished packaging, the containers used must be designed for proper cleaning and, if required, for sanitizing. Containers for salvaged finished product must be stored and handled so that they will not be contaminated.

Inspection of the transport vehicles delivering finished product is advisable, since unsanitary conditions could mean problems for the producer. The product or containers must be stored in a clean, dry location and protected from airborne contamination. Storage on floors or on cardboard, boards, or plastics laid on the floor incurs unwarranted risks.

Contamination control in the packaging area is critical. Accumulations of dust or other material that may become airborne should be prevented. This area, as well as the finished-product handling area, should have a positive air pressure to prevent airborne contamination from areas where air pressure is lower. Equipment must be clean, and filled containers, prior to sealing, must be protected from possible contamination. Walkways located over finished-product conveyors and airborne material are possible sources of such contamination.

The filled containers should be stored in a clean, dry area. If the product is one requiring refrigeration or freezing it must be moved promptly to the appropriate area. Equipment used to transport product to distribution outlets or distribution warehouses should be maintained in sanitary condition. If refrigeration is required, the carrier should be capable of maintaining the required temperature, for the required period of time. The producer must accept his responsibility for the product and must make an effort to assure proper handling from production to consumption. For this reason it is advisable in contracting for hauling to know whether the product in question will be handled along with other products that might jeopardize its safety. Warehouses should have satisfactory control programs to assure that products are properly handled and protected.

REWORK HANDLING

In many processing operations, products failing to meet quality specifications are salvaged by reprocessing. Where the over-all process includes a stage that will destroy salmonellae, the item being reprocessed should be inserted in the line ahead of this stage. In any event, precautions should be taken to prevent contamination. The reprocessing or rehydration of dehydrated products should be segregated from other facilities, because it is virtually impossible to prevent escape of such material into the surrounding area. Accumulation of dehydrated products increases the risk of contamination, all the more so if there is no subsequent step that will destroy microorganisms. Salvaged or reused containers constitute a hazard, especially if not of sanitary construction.

CODING

It is essential that the producer code all finished material so that it can be located if trouble develops, and in such detail that a portion of a production lot can be identified and segregated if necessary. Failure to apply proper legible coding may necessitate removal of a needlessly large volume of product from the market.

SLAUGHTERING FACILITIES

Installations for animal slaughter introduce complications not encountered in other food-processing plants: e.g., the facility handling raw carcasses, whether avian or mammalian, cannot rely on a process to kill the salmonellae; cross-contamination may occur since individuals handle many carcasses; and edible organs are usually collected in a common container, thus risking contamination of salmonella-free organs by contaminated ones.

Salmonella contamination of the skin surface and digestive tract of the living animal can be assumed. Interior muscle tissue from a healthy animal is virtually sterile, but each step in the slaughtering and handling operation adds to the risk of its contamination. Generally, the incidence of salmonellae in livestock on the farm is low, but as animals progress through the holding pens it increases. Modification in transportation, holding, and slaughtering schedules could greatly improve this situation.

Cured meat products are usually processed in such a manner as to destroy salmonellae, but there is danger of recontamination, e.g., personnel charged with handling raw product may also handle cured products. Cured product should be segregated from raw products.

The considerations of handling raw meat are also applicable to facilities slaughtering poultry. Defeathering, evisceration, and chilling operations can easily spread salmonellae from contaminated carcasses to clean ones. Each step in the operation can contribute to the problem.

LOCATING PROBLEM AREAS

To achieve effective control of salmonellae in food-production facilities, one must have a knowledge of environmental conditions. Operations should be studied to recognize points of potential contamination and growth of organisms. Sampling should include: (1) environmental samples, (2) in-process samples, and (3) finished-product samples. The processor should realize that control of the environment is his first line of defense, and that continued or excessive environmental contamination means probable contamination of in-process samples. The presence of organisms in the processing line indicates that the risk of finished product contamination is great.

So diverse are food products and processing procedures that it is infeasible to list details for each operation. In products subjected to terminal sterilization, risks are minimal, and products most likely to be contaminated should receive greatest attention. Classification of food products can help focus such attention, taking into account such factors as: (1) probability that organisms will be present in the product, (2) circumstances favoring growth of the organism in the product, (3) whether there will be terminal preparation by the consumer before ingestion, and (4) the record of previous infections traced to the product.

PRODUCTION IMPROVEMENT

Improvements in processing procedures and equipment offer potential for progress in controlling contamination of foods. Advances may not be simple, but with the technical knowledge available many problems can be resolved. Reference has been made to the 3A Standards for food-processing equipment, and already much has been accomplished by equipment design based on these recommendations. But they do not solve all problems. In the dehydrated food industry, finely divided air-borne particulate products represent a special difficulty that might be solved through better equipment design. In certain "instantizing" operations, improvements could be made in the rewetting, curing, and drying operations. Redesign of equipment to facilitate cleaning and sanitization would be beneficial.

Many processes necessitate contact of personnel with the food. Great stress has been laid on hand contact, but sneezing, coughing, and talking may also contribute to contamination. Development of processes and equipment that minimize human contact with the finished food product is needed.

Airborne contamination is a potential problem in many operations, and its prevention should have the attention of equipment designers.

Slaughtering and rendering operations offer challenging problems. Some have already been noted, but review and study by those directly involved in the specific industry would identify many more. Certainly current practices in plucking, evisceration, and chilling of poultry could be improved.

These are but a few examples of improvements that can be effected in the food-processing industry. It is interesting that many members of industry are now willing to share their knowledge of operations control with others. Such exchange of information can be of major value, particularly to the smaller processing companies.

INDUSTRY–REGULATORY RELATIONSHIPS

A review of the records of outbreaks of salmonellosis indicates that the majority result from improper handling and preparation rather than from unsatisfactory operations by the food processor. Industry representatives note the effort placed upon in-plant control, the large sums being spent, the losses incurred when products are condemned, and unfavorable publicity resulting from product recall and tend to wonder whether the incidence of infection has been significantly changed. Are efforts and funds being concentrated where they will be most effective? Although control of food preparation may be more complex and more difficult than industrial control, little may be accomplished if we fail at this point, as has been pointed out by Prost and Riemann[12]:

Control measures are, to a large extent, focused on food processing and hygiene, and involve recommendations concerning inspection and sanitation in food plants; control of milk and water supplies; egg pasteurization; improved methods of food processing and in mass preparation of meals; microbiological standards for foods; control and removal of human carriers from food plants, etc. It has also been suggested that the place to attack with the greatest hope is where the greatest convergence occurs, namely, immediately before consumption.

REFERENCES

1. "Ordinances and Code Regulating the Processing of Eggs and Egg Products," U.S. Department of Health, Education, and Welfare (1968).
2. Series of papers presented at National Confectioners Association (1968).
3. J. Silliker, *The Salmonella Problem in the Poultry Industry*, Institute of American Poultry Industries (1966).
4. *Food Service Sanitation Manual*, U.S. Department of Health, Education and Welfare (1962).
5. *Sanitation Standards for Smoked Fish Processing, Part 1, Fish Smoking Establishments*, U.S. Department of Health, Education, and Welfare and U.S. Department of the Interior (1967).
6. "Grade 'A' Pasteurized Milk Ordinance," U.S. Department of Health, Education, and Welfare (1965).
7. M. Houston, "Salmonella Can Be Controlled," *Canner/Packer, 136*, 60 (January 1967).
8. International Association of Milk, Food and Environmental Sanitarians, *3A Sanitary Standards*, Shelbyville, Indiana.
9. P. A. F. White and S. E. Smith, *High Efficiency Air Filtration*, Butterworth & Company, London (1964).
10. National Audio Visual Center (Annex), Chamblee, Georgia 30005. Attention: Film Distribution.
11. W. M. Hall and E. Borker, "In-Plant Testing for Pathogenic Bacteria," *Food Technol. 22*, 549 (1968).
12. E. Prost and H. Riemann. "Food-Borne Salmonellosis," *Ann. Rev. Microbiol. 21*:495 (1967).

Addendum: Examples of Food-Handling Practices That May Lead to Salmonella Contamination of Foods

This partial list of faulty food-handling practices is given here to reiterate the complexity of salmonella control and the necessity for continuous monitoring of operations.

MEAT PROCESSING

- Cross-contamination between external surfaces and the interior of the carcass during hide removal.
- Rupture of the intestines during the removal of viscera, leading to fecal contamination of meat surfaces.
- The use of knives, saws, and other implements to "break down" successive carcasses, without intervening decontamination.
- Cross-contamination between infected and uninfected organs by the veterinary inspector's hands and instruments during examination of the viscera.
- The use of tank carts for storing organs, such as livers, from a number of carcasses.
- The use of chutes for moving meat cuts from one department to another.
- The washing of intestines in areas adjacent to other meat products, resulting in contamination by aerosol.
- Contamination of the skin of slaughtered hogs with fecal material during the dehairing process.
- The location of sausage kitchens adjacent to sausage slicing and packaging departments, permitting cross-contamination between raw- and finished-product handling areas. This situation is compounded by the frequent careless action of personnel in both departments.
- Direct human contact with sliced sausage and bacon during the packaging operation; even with the most efficient packaging equipment, employees must "make weight" by adding slices to the package.
- Mass transportation of animals to stockyards and their maintenance in communal holding pens not amenable to proper sanitizing. It has been shown that the longer animals are held in the pens, the higher the incidence of infection.

POULTRY PROCESSING

● The problems encountered in meat processing are, for the most part, also present in the slaughtering and dressing of poultry. In addition, during poultry processing, carcasses are introduced into chill tanks, a "common bath" that permits cross-contamination between infected and uninfected carcasses.

● Defeathering and scalding processes may permit cross-contamination between infected and uninfected carcasses.

● Ice packing of poultry also permits cross-contamination between infected and uninfected carcasses, since when the ice melts the effect is that of a common bath.

● As with meat processing, edible organs may be held in common containers, permitting cross-contamination.

RENDERING

● The use of the same equipment for handling raw material and finished product, particularly in-plant trucks.

● The interchange of personnel between raw- and finished-product handling areas.

● Failure to separate raw- and finished-product handling areas.

● Failure to control moisture, such as condensate dripping from uninsulated water pipes onto dried product, permitting the development of foci of rapid bacterial multiplication.

● Failure to control rodents and insects.

"FURTHER PROCESSING" OF POULTRY AND MEAT PRODUCTS

● Frequently, in the production of boned poultry and other meats, the same person introduces the raw meat or poultry into the cook tank and subsequently removes it, thus providing the possibility for cross-contamination.

● Frequently, the discharge from the cooker is onto a table or belt situated near the raw material handling area, again permitting cross-contamination.

● Whenever the cooked product must be boned and diced, it involves many hand operations with ample opportunity for direct contamination.

● Lack of provision for protecting the boned product from contamination during the chilling operation can lead to air contamination, particularly if the product is cooled in an area where raw products are stored.

BAKERY OPERATIONS

● The use of checked, dirty, and ungraded eggs.
● The reuse of frozen-egg cans for scaling other ingredients in the bakery.
● Improper thawing of eggs. Frozen eggs should be properly thawed in cold running water or by holding at refrigerator temperatures. All too frequently, however, they are thawed at room temperature, and extensive bacterial multiplication occurs, even though the interior of the can may still contain unthawed egg.
● The storage of thawed eggs at room temperature during the operating day. The eggs then might be placed in a cooler overnight and returned to the processing area the following day.
● Failure to refrigerate perishable baked goods such as custard pies.
● The manufacture of uncooked toppings and meringues without taking into account the bacteriological condition of the raw materials. It is too often wrongly assumed that the browning process will destroy salmonellae in the meringue.

EGG PROCESSING

● Production of dried egg albumen requires that natural glucose be removed prior to drying. This is commonly done by "natural fermentation," a process that involves inoculating a vat with material from a previously fermented vat. The fermentation of egg albumen normally involves the growth of fecal streptoccoci, but there is also extensive growth of coliforms and salmonellae. In the routine processing of egg albumen, therefore, substantial numbers of salmonellae are routinely to be found in the fermented albumen prior to drying, because of the vat to vat transfer of the inoculum.
● Although the drying process destroys a substantial proportion of the salmonellae present in the fermented product, almost invariably the dried egg albumen contains some salmonellae and must be held in a "hot room" 7 to 10 days or longer at temperatures of approximately 130°F (55°C) to destroy remaining organisms. If the dried egg albumen is not

handled carefully between the dryer and the hot room the fine powder can contaminate working surfaces throughout the plant. Thus, if the untreated dried egg albumen is handled in an area close to the finished packaging room, both decontaminated albumen and "yellow products" are subjected to cross-contamination from the "fallout." This common occurrence can be prevented only through careful control of product movement.

• Enzyme treatment using commercial glucose oxidase (containing catalase) to convert the glucose to gluconic acid is an alternative to natural fermentation, hydrogen peroxide being added as a source of oxygen. If this treatment is not carefully controlled, substantial quantities of foam collect on the surface of the liquid. In this case the peroxide never finds its way into the mass of the liquid, which then ferments by "natural fermentation," and the foam forms a matrix in which extensive bacterial development can occur.

• Yellow products (yolk and whole egg) need not necessarily be desugared before drying. Frequently, however, liquid products are held in tanks located near those holding fermenting egg albumen, providing ample opportunity for cross-contamination. Further, even if the yellow products are pasteurized, they are frequently held in vats after pasteurization prior to canning, providing opportunity for cross-contamination via aerosols.

POWDER-COOLING OPERATIONS

• In certain phases of soybean processing, the oil is extracted from the seed to produce soybean protein flakes, which are cooled in rotary drums and then transported to silos. If the cooling air is contaminated with salmonellae, contamination of the flakes is inevitable. Further, there is a continuous circulation of air through the silos; and if the air is contaminated, organisms are carried into the finished product. There are a number of other "powder-cooling" operations that occur in food processing, e.g., the cooling of dried egg products, in which large volumes of air are used with attendant hazards.

MISCELLANEOUS

• Improper storage of perishable goods in retail bakeries is commonplace. The proprietors are generally cognizant of the risk of staphylococcus poisoning as a result of long-standing records of trouble with cream-filled pastries, but the potential for salmonellosis has not become firmly established. Such mishandling in manufacture as occurs in large commercial bakeries is even more commonplace in the smaller retail bakeries doing in-store manufacturing.

 • A number of commercial "synthetic" fillings for pies and various pastries have been merchandized in recent years. Although the claim has been made that these fillings will not support bacterial growth, it has been clearly demonstrated that they will indeed support substantial multiplication, including that of salmonellae. Manufacturers tend to claim that bakery goods containing such fillings need not be refrigerated, when in fact they are just as dangerous as "natural" fillings.

 • There is evidence that commercial dried dog foods are not infrequently contaminated with salmonellae. When these foods are rehydrated for use in the home, a nutrient medium suitable for growth of salmonellae is produced. It is common practice to offer such food to pets and if it is not immediately consumed to allow it to remain in feeding containers for many hours. This, plus the fact that washing of the feeding containers is generally not done carefully, may increase the salmonellae dosage to a highly infective level. This problem may well be a significant one with respect to transmission of salmonellosis to domestic animals and in turn to man, a possibility that has not been adequately assessed.

 • Fish are frequently flumed with contaminated seawater, a practice that has led to at least one major outbreak of salmonellosis.

 • There has been a tremendous increase in the preparation of food in retail grocery stores in recent years. The activity in many instances is unsupervised and may be carried out in virtual ignorance of proper food-handling principles. The outbreaks of salmonellosis traced to barbecued chickens in the Pacific Northwest is only one example. The cooked and highly perishable food frequently is not properly stored, foods that should be refrigerated are permitted to remain at room temperature, and foods that are supposedly held in the "warm state" are generally maintained at a temperature permitting rapid bacterial multiplication. The usual delicatessen handling such products makes no provision to prevent cross-contamination between raw and cooked foods. It is indeed surprising that more outbreaks are not traced to this source, but this freedom from involvement in food poisoning may be more apparent than real. The stores preparing such food are not subject to federal inspection and in most instances local inspection is virtually nonexistent.

 • Butcher shops may well be an important factor in the spread of salmonellosis. It is common for butchers to handle raw meats and then to slice and package processed meats, which must inevitably lead to the contamination of foods that are usually consumed without further cooking. Instances of salmonellosis traceable to this source would ordinarily go undiagnosed and unreported.

9 Destruction of Salmonellae and Prevention of Growth

To minimize the hazards of an infectious disease, particularly one such as salmonellosis that may be food-borne, it is necessary to know the environmental conditions under which the causative organism will grow and persist in the absence of the host and to develop practicable methods for destroying the infective agent so that it can be barred from or removed from the host's food or environment.

Members of the genus *Salmonella* belong to the family Enterobacteriaceae, and they possess all cultural, growth, and morphological characteristics generally associated with this family. They do not form spores, and the cells are only moderately heat resistant. They are considered to be facultative anaerobes, and therefore by definition they possess both oxidative and fermentative mechanisms for obtaining energy. They grow more readily and extensively under aerobic conditions, however. Their nutritional requirements are not exacting, and they are capable of growing in or on most foods or feeds that are moist and do not have sufficient concentrations of acids, salts, or other substances to act as preservatives.

The some 1,300 *Salmonella* serotypes have not all been studied in detail as regards the effect of environmental extremes on growth and survival or death. Nevertheless, among those that have been investigated there exists a remarkable homogeneity from one serotype to another. Variations in heat resistance have been recognized among strains, but unusual resistance is not peculiar to any one serotype. Mediation by the R factor to effect changes in resistance toward heat, chemicals, and other environmental factors deserves further study.

126

GROWTH

Although the temperature range for growth of salmonellae is considered to lie between 45°F (7°C) and 113°F (45°C) with an optimum temperature for growth (shortest generation time) at approximately 95–99°F (35–37°C), growth can occur beyond this range, but at considerably reduced rates or to a lesser extent. Angelotti et al.[1] noted that a mixed culture containing serotypes Senftenberg strain 775W, Enteritidis, and Manhattan grew in chicken a la king at 44°F (7°C) but not at 42°F (6°C). No growth occurred at 50°F (10°C), however, in custard or ham salad even though the salmonellae were capable of growing in these foods at more favorable temperatures. These studies essentially confirmed those of Prescott and Geer[2] and Prescott and Tanner,[3] who claimed that a temperature of 41°F (5°C) or below was required to completely prevent growth of salmonellae in foods.

Angelotti et al.[4] reported that mixed cultures of salmonellae grew in chicken a la king and custard at 114°F (45°C) but not at 116°F (46°C). The cultures failed to grow in ham salad at these elevated temperatures. Thus, the extremes in growth temperature range for salmonellae thus far tested lie between 44°F (7°C) and 114°F (45°C). As demonstrated by Angelotti et al.,[1,4] however, interaction of factors will influence the extremes in environmental conditions under which the salmonellae will grow. For example, salt concentrations that will not prevent growth at more favorable temperatures may lower the maximum temperature for growth below that known to pertain under ideal conditions.

For those strains tested, salmonellae can grow within a pH range of about 4.1 to 9.0. Optimum pH lies between 6.5 and 7.5. Banwart and Ayres[5] reported that serotypes Pullorum, Oranienberg, and Senftenberg failed to grow at pH 9.0 and above. The minimum pH that permits growth is influenced by the nature of the acid present. The weak organic acids appear to have specific inhibitory properties above that effected by increased hydrogen ion concentration.

Growth of salmonellae in foods can be inhibited if sufficiently high levels of salts or sugars are added. Koelensmid and van Rhee[6] reported that salmonellae failed to grow in meat products containing salt concentrations higher than 7 percent. The effects of salts and sugars upon growth inhibition are best expressed in terms of water activity (a_w), defined as the ratio of the vapor pressures of the solution to solvent (water). A lowering of water activity, then, can be effected by increasing the soluble solids in the food or growth medium. Christian and Scott[7] reported that the range of water activities permitting growth of 16 strains of salmonellae was substantially unaffected by the nature and composition of nutrients in the growth medium. The lowest a_w that permitted growth of salmonellae was 0.94 (equivalent approximately to a 9 percent sodium chloride solution). No evidence was found to indicate that salmonellae could be "trained" to grow at lower levels of a_w.

Although most domestically produced cured meats have insufficient concentrations of added salt to prevent growth of salmonellae, they are very rarely found to harbor these microorganisms. The combination of adequate cooking temperatures, presence of curing agents in addition to salt, and the practice of holding the meats at low temperatures to extend shelf life seemingly explains their relative freedom from salmonella contamination.

SURVIVAL

When compared to other bacterial species the salmonellae appear not to possess unusual ability to survive under environmental conditions that do not permit growth. Nevertheless, their ability to survive for relatively long periods of time in chilled, frozen, or dried foods and feeds must be taken into consideration from a public health standpoint.

Buttiaux and Moriamez[8] noted a 20 percent survival of a *Salmonella* population in refrigerated curing brines for ham and bacon after 15 days. It is well recognized that salmonellae remain viable for long periods of time in frozen foods. McClesky and Christopher[9] reported survival of five serotypes after 5 months in sliced, sweetened, frozen strawberries. Schneider and Gunderson[10] recovered viable salmonellae from eviscerated frozen poultry after prolonged storage. Browne[11] reported that salmonellae survived for at least 13 months on poultry carcasses that had been quick frozen at −35°F (−37°C) and stored at −5°F (−21°C).

In his review, Gibson[12] cites a number of references to indicate that serotype Dublin is capable of remaining viable for over 1,000 days in dried bovine feces stored in the laboratory; for 120 days in pasture soil; 87 days in tap water; and 115 days in contaminated pond water. Also, serotype Typhimurium survived up to 120 days in water and 280 days in garden soil. Various serotypes survived 2–6 weeks at room temperature on contaminated vegetables and up to 28 months in dried, naturally infected bird feces.

That salmonellae can persist for prolonged periods at ambient temperatures in dried nonfat milk, egg products, and rendered animal byproducts is well documented. There is also considerable evidence that they can survive for long periods in environmental dusts in food-production plants and that they can persist, and perhaps grow in deposits and litter of swine holding pens.[13] It is to be expected that they would persist reasonably well, or even grow under some conditions, in such media as waste water, poultry water containing mash, wet feedstuffs, and barnyard soils.[12]

There appears to be no reliable index to predict survival of salmonellae in the frozen or dried state because of the many interrelated factors (initial numbers, moisture level, and temperature, for example). Generally, freezing or drying reduces the viable salmonellae population in foods, but the survivors of the treatment die at a relatively low rate thereafter.

DEATH

Ordinary pasteurizing or cooking times and temperatures generally are considered adequate to kill salmonellae in foods having a high moisture content. In most instances foods that are to be heat processed can be made completely safe with respect to salmonella contamination without impairing the quality of the food. There are exceptions, however. Fresh meats and poultry cannot be heat processed sufficiently to kill salmonellae and yet retain the quality and appearance of the unprocessed meat. Functional properties of egg products are easily damaged by excessive heat treatment. It is necessary to subject them to the minimum heat treatment that will provide reasonable safety.

The effectiveness of a heat treatment is measured by determining the length of time that is necessary at a specified temperature to kill 90 percent of the organisms originally present (time necessary for the survivors to traverse one log cycle). The time, generally termed the D value or decimal reduction time, can be experimentally estimated for a given microorganism by inspection of the exponential death curve at a given temperature or more precisely by calculation. The preferred method of calculation is that proposed by Schmidt.[14] In heat processing studies, thermal death times (TDT) (defined as the minimum time necessary at a specific temperature to reduce a given population to below detectable levels) may be determined. For salmonella investigations, 140°F (60°C) is often employed to express TDT values, and the experimental initial populations most often lie between 10^6 and 10^8 cells per ml. The symbol "F_{140}" is used to indicate the TDT at 140°F.

D values (or TDT values) can be determined under a single set of conditions but at different temperatures and used to plot a thermal resistance curve (log D versus temperature in °F). An illustrative thermal resistance curve is shown in Figure 11. The slope of the line measured in

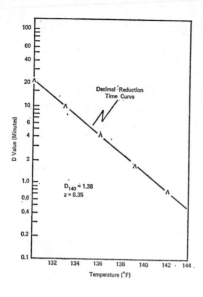

FIGURE 11 Thermal resistance curve for a serotype Oranienburg strain determined in liquid whole egg, pH 5.5. Adapted from a similar figure by Anellis *et al.*[15]

°F is denoted as z, which is in effect the increase in processing temperature in °F required to reduce the D value through one log cycle (90 percent reduction). The establishment of z values for a given microorganism is convenient in that it allows the calculation of equivalent thermal processes at different temperatures. The z values determined for salmonellae in aqueous media range between 7 and 11, usually 8 to 9. For example, if 3.5 min at 140°F is considered to be an adequate process and $z = 8$, then 0.35 min at 148°F or 35 min at 132°F would be considered equivalent processes.

The D value for most salmonellae in whole egg at 140°F is generally considered to be about 0.4 min (see *Egg Pasteurization Manual,* Review Copy, USDA, Agr. Res. Service. Western Util. Res. Develop. Div., Albany, Calif., 1967). D values vary considerably, however, among strains and can be influenced greatly by pH, sugar or salt content (a_w), or physiological state of the cells. Also, the nature of the recovery medium employed to estimate the number of surviving cells may greatly influence calculated D values. Noninhibitory media generally yield a higher recovery of the heat-injured cells (yielding a higher calculated D value) than do many of the commonly employed *Salmonella* plating media that contain inhibitory substances.[15,16] Care must be taken, therefore, in drawing specific conclusions about the heat resistance of salmonellae.

Ng[17] determined the heat sensitivity of 300 cultures of salmonellae representing 75 different serotypes and compared their sensitivities to a reference strain, serotype Typhimurium TM-1. He found a remarkable agreement in heat sensitivity among most of the strains. The D value for the reference strain determined at 134.6°F (57°C) and pH 6.8 in a trypticase soy medium was 1.2 min. The average resistance of almost all the strains was 1.2 times that of TM-1. The least-resistant strain was slightly more than half as resistant, and the most resistant was a serotype Blockley strain (5 times as resistant as the reference strain).

Winter et al.[18] isolated from eggs a strain of serotype Senftenberg designated as 775W, which has remarkable heat resistance and which has therefore been employed as a reference strain. This strain is variously reported as being 10 to 20 times as heat resistant as most other serotypes. Ng[17] reported this strain to have a D value of 31 min at 134.6°F (57°C) as compared with 1.2 min for his reference Typhimurium strain. Nineteen other Senftenberg strains tested had heat resistances similar to serotype Typhimurium. It has been concluded generally that serotype Senftenberg 775W represents a most unusual and rare mutant, and that heat-processing schedules of foods should not necessarily be based on this one strain. However, Davidson et al.[19] have reported isolating a second Senftenberg strain from meat having heat resistance very similar to strain 775W. Whether heat-resistant Salmonella mutants commonly exist is a subject worthy of further study. Similar heat-resistant mutants occur among other bacterial species (e.g., Reference 20).

The most extensive and exacting studies of heat resistance in salmonellae in liquid egg products have been conducted by Anellis et al.[15] and Osborne et al.[21] As an outgrowth of these studies, as well as others, a pasteurization process is now available and forms the basis of a regulation (published in the Federal Register, January 1, 1967) to the effect that "Strained and filtered liquid whole egg shall be flash heated to not less than 140°F and held at this temperature for not less than 3½ minutes." Sugihara et al.[22] reported that more than 10^7 per ml of added serotype Typhimurium cells were destroyed in 2 min at 140°F (60°C), but that Senftenberg 775W survived in considerable numbers.

Thus, a method has been devised for the heat treatment of liquid egg products that will destroy essentially all the contaminating salmonellae and yet retain the product's functional properties. A refinement of the process has been developed for egg whites[23] through the adjustment of the pH to 6.6–7.0 with lactic acid, addition of aluminum salts to protect the egg proteins from denaturation, and pasteurization usually at 140°F (60°C) for 3.5 min. This refined process minimizes any changes in the functional properties of the egg whites. Slightly more severe thermal processing is generally practiced for egg yolks and for sugared and salted yolk (see Egg Pasteurization Manual, Review Copy, USDA,

Agr. Res. Service, Western Util. Res. Develop. Div., Albany, Calif., 1967).

Similar, but less effective, heat-processing methods for pasteurizing liquid egg white have been proposed, ranging downward to 134°F (56.7°C) for 3.5 min, with or without the addition of a whipping aid.[24]

Functional properties of nonfat dried milk are not so critically affected by heat treatment of the milk prior to drying. Therefore, effective pasteurization sufficient to destroy salmonellae prior to drying can be undertaken.

Several investigators have noted the marked effect of pH upon the D values obtained for serotypes of *Salmonella*. For example, when salmonellae are suspended in liquid whole egg, D values decrease as the pH is increased from pH 5.5 to 8.2.[21] Differences in pH apparently account in part for the greater heat resistance in egg yolk than in egg white. If liquid whole egg is acidified by a strong acid such as HCl, the pH for maximum heat resistance is 5.5 or below. On the other hand, if acidification is achieved by the addition of weak organic acids, e.g., acetic or lactic, a decrease in heat resistance is noted.[25]

Several of the organic acids, including lactic and the fatty acid series, are known to exert a lethal effect upon salmonellae, even without the application of heat. Ayres[26] noted that lemon juice (pH 2.3) and lime juice (pH 2.5) killed added salmonellae within a few minutes. On the other hand, salmonellae survived in chilled tomato juice (pH 4.3–4.4) up to 30 days. Kintner and Mangel[27] noted that six different strains of *Salmonella* were killed within 2 hours when inoculated into salad dressing adjusted to pH 3.4 with acetic acid. However, four of the six strains survived 24 hours at pH 4.56. Hinshelwood[28] also noted a rapid kill of salmonellae at room temperature in salad dressing at pH values less than 4.0. As a result of such observations, unpasteurized eggs generally are considered to be safe in the commercial manufacture of mayonnaise and salad dressings of specified compositions. Undoubtedly, greater advantage can be taken of the capacity of organic acids in both foods and animal feeds, either with or without heat, to reduce the incidence of contamination and thereby aid in alleviating the salmonella problem. It is perhaps no coincidence that little hazard exists from salmonella contamination in such foods as acid vegetables and fruits.

In line with what is known of other bacterial species, an increase in heat resistance of salmonellae results from a reduction of a_w of the suspending medium, either through removal of water or by addition of solutes such as salts and sugars. For example, heat resistance of salmonellae is about tenfold greater in sugared or salted egg yolk than in whole egg (Garibaldi, unpublished results, quoted in USDA *Egg Pasteurization Manual,* Review Copy, Western Util. Res. Dev. Div., Albany, Calif., 1967).

Although few definitive data have yet been published, it would be expected that heat resistance of salmonella would progressively and markedly increase as a_w levels approach dryness. For example, Rasmussen et al.[29] reported that a heat treatment of 180°F (82°C) for 7 min was required to kill Bredeney or Derby serotypes in meat meal containing 6 percent moisture and naturally contaminated with one viable cell per gram. A heat treatment of 170°F (76.7°C) for 15 min was required to kill one Montevideo cell per 2 g and 195°F (90.6°C) for 7 min to kill serotype Montevideo at an initial contaminating level of 25 cells per gram. Surprisingly, when 2,000 serotype Senftenberg 775W cells per gram were added to meat meal having similar moisture content, a heat treatment of 155°F (68°C) for 15 min reduced the population to below detectable levels. Thus, microorganisms having relatively high heat resistance in a moist environment do not necessarily also have a proportionately higher heat resistance in a dry environment.

Goepfert[16] reported surprisingly high heat resistance of a serotype Typhimurium test strain when lyophilized cells were heated in milk chocolate having a very low moisture content. For example, D values at 158°F (70°C), 176°F (80°C), and 194°F (90°C) were 816, 222, and 75, respectively ($z = 34.2$). Again, serotype Senftenberg 775W was less heat resistant than the Typhimurium strain when tested in the dry state under similar conditions.

Ayres and Slosberg[30] and Banwart and Ayres[31] demonstrated the effectiveness of dry heat treatment at 120, 130, and 135°F (49, 54.5, and 57°C) on reducing salmonella infection in pan-dried egg white. These research results, as well as industry experience, indicate that holding dry egg white containing 6 percent moisture at 125–130°F (51.7–54.5°C) for 7 to 10 days after the product has reached the required temperature kills salmonellae without greatly affecting the product's functional properties. Similar treatment is effective in rendered animal by-products and is practiced to some extent in Europe.

Thus, D values of salmonellae can be greatly influenced by many factors. In keeping with what is known generally for other microorganisms, Ng[32] reported that *Salmonella* cells from the exponential growth phase (physiologically young) are less heat resistant than those in the stationary phase (physiologically old). Also, a direct relationship was observed between heat resistance and the temperature at which the cells tested were grown. Taking such factors into consideration as strain selection, physiological state, growth temperature, pH, and nature of suspending medium, a several hundredfold difference in heat resistance can be demonstrated among the extremes of *Salmonella* strains, even at high water activities. These recognized differences must be taken into consideration in designing effective heat treatments for destroying salmonellae. Nevertheless, for most cooked foods in which heat processing does not greatly affect quality, these differences in heat resistance become unimportant.

Chemical methods have been proposed for destroying salmonellae in heat-labile egg products. Ayres and Slosberg[30] demonstrated that hydrogen peroxide was effective in egg white at ambient temperatures. A patented procedure has been described[32] for treating egg white with 0.05 percent peroxide at 125°F (51.7°C) for 2 min, followed by destruction of the peroxide with catalase.

Fumigation of dried egg products with the epoxides, ethylene and propylene oxides, has been suggested by Sair.[33] These gases have been used for bactericidal treatment of spices, gums, and other materials. Their effectiveness is influenced by the moisture content of the dried product. In the presence of chlorides these epoxides leave residual chlorohydrins in the product, and they have not been approved for egg powder treatment. Beta-propiolactone, another epoxide, has received attention but not approval as a possible bactericidal agent for the treatment of liquid egg products.

Treatment of liquid egg products with high-energy radiations to kill salmonellae was first proposed by Proctor's group,[34] and their results were later extended by European investigators.[35-38] Gamma irradiation sources, however, are not generally available to the egg processor, and doses sufficient to attain adequate kill of salmonellae (0.2–0.5 Mrad) may produce undesirable flavors in the treated product. Long-term animal feeding tests to demonstrate safety of irradiated egg products would be required by regulatory officials prior to acceptance of this processing method.

Treatment of thin films of liquid egg products with ultraviolet light to destroy salmonellae has been proposed by Oppenheimer *et al.*[39] Adequate treatment, however, also produces undesirable flavors and odors in the product.

In the thermal processing of low-acid foods to achieve relative safety from botulism episodes the so-called 12D concept is advocated and generally practiced. This concept is based on the principle that all such foods should receive thermal processing theoretically sufficient to reduce the population level through 12 log cycles of the most heat-resistant *Clostridium botulinum* spores. Although many such thermally processed foods are damaged because of the required severe heat processing, the concept has proved to be extremely valuable in virtually eliminating the occurrence of botulism as a result of underprocessing.

One might suppose that a similar concept for the destruction of salmonellae could be applied to thermally processed heat labile foods such as liquid egg products. Serotype Senftenberg strain 775W then would become the reference strain to which the 12D concept is applied. Such a stringent course of action appears unwarranted, because it might result in making all thermal processing methods thus far proposed impracticable for the treatment of egg products.

That the two recognized heat-resistant mutant strains of *Salmonella* thus far discovered belong to a single serotype is most likely mere coincidence. As marginal thermal processing for heat labile foods gains more general acceptance, it is possible that similar heat-resistant mutants among other serotypes will be discovered.

REFERENCES

1. R. Angelotti, E. Wilson, M. J. Foter, and K. H. Lewis, "Time-Temperature Effects on Salmonellae and Staphylococci in Foods. I. Behavior in Broth Cultures and Refrigerated Foods," *Robert A. Taft Sanitary Eng. Center Tech. Rep. F59-2*, U.S. Dep. Health, Education, and Welfare, PHS (1959).
2. S. C. Prescott, and L. P. Geer, "Observations on Food-Poisoning Organisms under Refrigeration Conditions," *Refrig. Eng.*, *32*, 211 (1936).
3. S. C. Prescott and F. W. Tanner, "Microbiology in Relation to Food Preservation," *Food Res.*, *3*, 189 (1938).
4. R. Angelotti, M. J. Foter, and K. H. Lewis, "Time-Temperature Effects on Salmonellae and Staphylococci in Foods. II. Behavior at Warm Holding Temperatures. Thermal-Death-Time Studies," *Robert A. Taft Sanitary Eng. Center Tech. Rep. F60-5*, U.S. Dep. Health, Education, and Welfare, PHS (1960).
5. G. J. Banwart and J. C. Ayres, "The Effect of pH on the Growth of Salmonella and Functional Properties of Liquid Egg White," *Food Technol.*, *11*, 244 (1957).
6. W. A. A. B. Koelensmid and R. van Rhee, "*Salmonella* in Meat Products," *Ann. Inst. Pasteur Lille*, *15*, 85 (1964).
7. J. H. B. Christian and W. J. Scott, "Water Relations of Salmonellae at 30°C," *Australian J. Biol. Sci.*, *6*, 565 (1953).
8. R. Buttiaux and J. Moriamez, "The Microbiology of Fish and Meat Curing Brines," pp. 247–262, in *Proc. 2nd Int. Symp. Food Microbiol.*, London (1957).
9. C. S. McClesky and W. N. Christopher, "Some Factors Influencing the Survival of Pathogenic Bacteria in Cold-Pack Strawberries," *Food Res.*, *6*, 327 (1941).
10. M. D. Schneider and M. F. Gunderson, "Investigators Shed More Light on *Salmonella* Problems," *U.S. Egg Poult. Mag.*, *55*, 10, 22 (1949).

11. A. S. Browne, "The Public Health Significance of *Salmonella* on Poultry and Poultry Products," PhD Dissertation, Univ. of California (1949).
12. E. A. Gibson, "Reviews of the Progress of Dairy Science. Section E. Diseases of Dairy Cattle. *Salmonella* Infection in Cattle," *J. Dairy Res., 32*, 97 (1965).
13. L. Leistner, J. Johantges, R. H. Deibel, and C. F. Niven, Jr., "The Occurrence and Significance of Salmonellae in Meat Animals and Animal By-product Feeds," pp. 9–20, in *Proc. 13th Conf., Am. Meat Inst. Found.* (1961).
14. C. F. Schmidt, "Thermal Resistance of Microorganisms," Chap. 32, in *Antiseptics, Disinfectants, Fungicides and Sterilization*, G. Reddish, ed., Lea and Febiger, Philadelphia, (1954).
15. A. Anellis, J. Lubas, and M. M. Rayman, "Heat Resistance in Liquid Eggs of Some Strains of the Genus *Salmonella*," *Food Res. 19*, 377 (1954).
16. J. M. Goepfert and R. A. Biggie, "Heat Resistance of Salmonella Typhimurium and Salmonella Senftenberg 775W in Chocolate," *Appl. Microbiol. 16*, 1939 (1968).
17. H. Ng, "Heat Sensitivity of 300 *Salmonella* Isolates," pp. 39–41 in *U.S. Dep. Agr., Agr. Res. Ser. ARS 74-37*, (1966).
18. A. R. Winter, G. F. Stewart, V. H. McFarlane, and M. Solowey, "Pasteurization of Liquid Egg Products. III. Destruction of *Salmonella* in Liquid Whole Egg," *Am. J. Pub. Health, 36*, 451 (1946).
19. C. M. Davidson, M. Boothroyd, and D. L. Georgala, "Thermal Resistance of *Salmonella senftenberg*," *Nature, 212*, 1060 (1966).
20. C. F. Niven Jr., L. G. Buettner, and J. B. Evans, "Thermal Tolerance Studies on the Heterofermentative Lactobacilli that Cause Greening of Cured Meat Products," *Appl. Microbiol., 2*, 26 (1954).
21. W. W. Osborne, R. P. Straka, and H. Lineweaver, "Heat Resistance of Strains of *Salmonella* in Liquid Whole Egg, Egg Yolk, and Egg White," *Food Res., 19*, 451 (1954).
22. T. F. Sugihara, K. Ijichi, and L. Kline, "Heat Pasteurization of Liquid Whole Egg," *Food Technol., 20*, 1076 (1966).
23. F. E. Cunningham, "Process for Pasteurizing Liquid Egg White," pp. 61–65, in *U.S. Dep. Agr., Agr. Res. Ser. ARS 74-37* (1966).
24. L. Kline, T. F. Sugihara, and K. Ijichi, "Further Studies on Heat Pasteurization of Raw Liquid Egg White," *Food Technol., 20*, 1604 (1966).
25. J. A. Garibaldi, "Factors Affecting the Heat Sensitivity of Salmonellae," pp. 34–37, in *U.S. Dep. Agr., Agr. Res. Ser. ARS 74-37* (1966).
26. J. C. Ayres, "The Survival of Pathogenic Bacteria and Other Microorganisms in Fruit Juices," *Thesis*, Univ. of Illinois Library, Urbana (1942).
27. T. C. Kintner and M. Mangel, "Survival of Staphylococci and Salmonellae Experimentally Inoculated into Salad Dressing Prepared with Dried Eggs," *Food Res. 18*, 6 (1953).
28. C. Hinshelwood, "Decline and Death of Bacterial Populations," *Nature, 167*, 666 (1951).
29. O. G. Rasmussen, R. Hansen, N. J. Jacobs, and O. H. M. Wilder, "Dry Heat Resistance of Salmonellae in Rendered Animal By-products," *Poultry Sci., 43*, 1151 (1964).
30. J. C. Ayres and H. M. Slosberg, "Destruction of *Salmonella* in Egg Albumen," *Food Technol., 3*, 180 (1949).

31. G. J. Banwart and J. C. Ayres, "The Effect of High Temperature Storage on the Content of *Salmonella* and on Functional Properties of Dried Egg White," *Food Technol., 10,* 68 (1956).
32. H. Ng, "Factors Affecting the Heat Resistance of *Salmonella*," Abstract from presentation at the Joint AOCS–AACC Meeting, Washington, D.C. (Apr. 3, 1968).
33. L. Sair, "Sensitivity of Salmonellae to Epoxides," pp. 41–47, in *U.S. Dep. Agr., Agr. Res. Ser. ARS 74-37* (1966).
34. J. T. R. Nickerson, S. E. Charm, R. C. Brogle, E. E. Lockhart, B. E. Proctor, and H. Lineweaver, "Use of High Voltage Cathode Rays to Destroy Bacteria of the Salmonella Group in Liquid and Frozen Egg White and Egg White Solids," *Food Technol., 11,* 159 (1957).
35. J. Brooks, R. S. Hannan, and B. C. Hobbs, "Irradiation of Eggs and Egg Products," *Int. J. Appl. Radiat. Isotopes, 6,* 149 (1959).
36. M. Ingram, D. N. Rhodes, and F. J. Ley, "The Use of Ionizing Radiation for the Elimination of Salmonellae from Frozen Whole Egg," AERE-3811. L.T.R.S. Record Memo No. 365. Isotope Res. Div. (AERE), Wantage Research Lab., Berkshire, England (1961).
37. F. J. Ley, B. M. Freeman, and B. C. Hobbs, "The Use of Gamma Radiation for the Elimination of Salmonellae from Various Foods," *J. Hyg., 61,* 515 (1963).
38. D. A. A. Mossell, "The Destruction of Salmonella Bacteria in Refrigerated Whole Egg with Gamma Radiation," *Int. J. Appl. Radiat. Isotopes, 9,* 109 (1960).
39. F. Oppenheimer, E. Benesi, and A. R. Taylor, "The Ultraviolet Irradiation of Biological Fluids in Thin-flowing Films," *Am. J. Pub. Health, 49,* 903 (1959).

10 Industry Controls

The presence of undesirable microorganisms, including salmonellae, in foods and drugs can generally be traced to one of three difficulties: (1) processing failure, (2) the use of contaminated raw materials, and (3) postprocessing contamination.

PROCESSING FAILURE

There is a wide variety of food and drug products that must be manufactured from raw materials that are likely to be contaminated with salmonellae. The transformation of such raw materials into satisfactory finished products requires application of a decontamination procedure, e.g., pasteurization, acidification, salting, or solvent treatment. If the decontamination procedure employed is inadequate, the contaminants present in the raw material are carried into the finished product.

Processing failure has, on numerous occasions, been traced to the unwarranted assumption that a given procedure was destructive to salmonellae. For example, although heat treatment of dry products is an exceedingly slow and inefficient means of destroying microorganisms, on occasion it has been incorrectly assumed that dry heat application to a product adequately decontaminated it. It should be emphasized that most chemical and physical treatments have finite efficiencies with respect to microbial destruction, i.e., they are designed to deal with average (or usual) levels of contamination expected in raw materials. If questionable ingredients are used, the process designed to handle average contamination may no longer be adequate to ensure a satisfactory product. In this situation, then, processing failure is due to use of raw materials that cannot be effectively decontaminated by the process applied.

CONTAMINATED RAW MATERIALS

The use of contaminated raw materials is a frequent cause of finished-product adulteration. If ingredients are incorporated into finished food products without application of intervening steps to eliminate contamination, the wholesomeness of the finished product is a reflection of the wholesomeness of individual ingredients used in manufacture. If each of the raw materials is free of salmonellae, then a satisfactory finished product can be made without dependence upon either physical or chemical decontamination in the manufacturing procedure.

The difficulty in many food products that have been shown to be contaminated with salmonellae can be traced to a single contaminated raw ingredient. The candy industry provides some excellent examples. Here contaminated coloring matter, desiccated coconut, dried milk, stabilizers, and nutmeats have each at one time or another been responsible for contamination of a finished product. In these instances, the manufacturer had relied on the supplier to deliver a product free of salmonellae; his procedure for making the candy did not provide for decontamination.

POSTPROCESSING CONTAMINATION

This term refers to contamination of a finished product from environmental sources. This may occur as a result of failure to separate raw- and finished-product handling areas. For example, raw meats frequently contain numbers of salmonellae, and if they are handled in close proximity to finished products, the aerosols that are created may contaminate finished goods. Cross-contamination between raw and processed egg products frequently occurs.

Contaminated air supplies leading to processing facilities have been found to be the direct cause of finished-product contamination. Air passing over locations where raw materials are being unloaded may pick up contaminated dust particles. Adjoining plants, handling contaminated raw ingredients, may also lead to air contamination, as also may animals such as rodents and birds that nest on the ledges of buildings.

The foregoing discussion indicates four distinct areas where control procedures might be applied: (1) environment, (2) raw materials, (3) processing, and (4) finished products. The most effective and economical points of control depend on the composition of a particular product and the technology used in making it. The points of emphasis will vary from plant to plant and also from time to time within a given operation.

For example, raw-material inspection constitutes the first line of defense in the manufacture of chocolate candies, since the processing cannot be depended on to eliminate salmonellae in contaminated ingredients. The prudent manufacturer will hold all critical ingredients until he has evidence that they constitute no salmonella hazard. Process control and sampling finished product are definitely secondary to raw-material inspection.

Contrast with the above the difficulties facing the renderer, the manufacturer of glandular-derived pharmaceutical products, and the food processor converting red meats and poultry into precooked frozen foods. In each instance, the basic raw material consists of animal tissue that must be assumed to be contaminated, in some degree, with salmonellae, and thus the finding of salmonellae is expected. In addition the bacteriological sampling of such raw materials poses a virtually insurmountable problem. The utilization of such raw materials demands an effective process control program that will answer, on a continuing basis, the question, "Does the decontamination step (or steps) effectively destroy salmonellae in the raw material?" For, without effective decontamination, the finished product will inevitably be adulterated.

Similarly, the egg processor must concern himself with the effectiveness of his pasteurization procedure. But, since the time–temperature relationships that are practical for certain egg products are only marginal with respect to destruction of salmonellae, the level of contamination in the raw material is of considerable significance in determining the effectiveness of the pasteurization procedure. Likewise, if salmonellae are to be eliminated in dried egg albumen by exposure at elevated temperatures, as is the practice in the industry, then the holding period required is a direct function of the number of salmonellae in the untreated product.

ENVIRONMENTAL CONTROL

Regardless of the product being manufactured, or the process involved, an effective and continuing campaign against contamination of the environment is an absolute necessity. If the environment is contaminated, finished product will inevitably become contaminated, regardless of the microbiological quality of raw materials or the efficiency of processing in the destruction of salmonellae. Surveillance of the environment must be carried out on a continuing and regular basis. The absence of positive findings is no license for terminating environmental surveillance.

The environmental surveillance program must take into account both the exterior and interior of the processing plant. In this regard, regular sampling and analysis of the air entering a plant provides highly significant information with respect to both external and internal plant environment. In cases where air enters the plant through filters, analysis of filter materials will indicate whether the environs of the plant constitute a salmonella threat. If salmonellae are present in the intake filters, it may be presumed that the interior of the plant is likewise contaminated, and the sources of contamination must be found and eliminated. They may be many and varied: e.g., spillover from trucks and railway cars delivering raw materials, neighboring processing plants, domestic animals housed near the plant, and wild animals roosting or nesting on the plant.

Air sampling is likewise effective in assessing the internal plant environment. Again, intake and exhaust air filters constitute excellent sampling points. Indeed, where such filters do not exist, it has proved convenient to install a fan either behind or in front of a filter cloth to secure a sample representative of air in the plant environment. Such samples not only permit an evaluation of the air coming into the plant but also indicate whether cross-contamination between raw and finished products is occurring *within* the plant.

The contents of vacuum cleaners and dust collectors, as well as floor sweepings, provide still other sampling points. Such materials are highly reflective of the internal environment of the processing plant, and if salmonellae are found in such samples the processor should be immediately alert to the likelihood of trouble in the finished product. Unfortunately, in some plants, contaminated vacuum cleaners can serve as a means of cross-contamination between departments. Obviously, it would be prudent to use separate vacuum cleaners for each processing area; if this is done, vacuum cleaner contents are among the best possible sampling points. It would be highly beneficial if methods could be developed for the daily sterilization of vacuum cleaners, as, for example, with ethylene oxide. This would eliminate vacuum cleaners as potential continuing sources of contamination and would provide a useful environmental sampling point.

In certain food-processing operations there are sampling points that are so indicative of the microbiological quality of the finished product that, to some extent, they constitute an even more useful quality-control sample than the finished product. Examples of this are the "scrap" or "salvage" that is an inevitable by-product of many candy-making operations, the "sifter-tailings" from milk and egg drying operations, the overflow from equipment packaging dry food materials, and scrapings from meat slicing equipment. Such materials are of virtually the same chemical composition as the finished product, they have been subjected to the same processing steps, and they are more amenable to representative sampling than are many packaged finished products. In addition, they have had a greater total exposure to the plant environment, since they flow less rapidly and accumulate on equipment surfaces. In this sense, they not only provide samples from which to gauge the microbiology of the finished product, but they also more faithfully mirror the potential for environmental contamination of the finished product than does the product itself. Experience has taught that a salmonella problem can be more readily detected by examining these materials than by examining the finished product. On many occasions, positive results have been obtained on sifter-tailings and scrap material when results of initial tests on corresponding finished products were negative, and more exhaustive sampling of the finished product stimulated by these results has disclosed the presence of salmonellae.

An effective environmental surveillance program is the prime requisite for total salmonella control in virtually any food-processing operation, with the possible exception of plants producing retorted canned products. The desirability of a raw-material inspection program depends, in large measure, upon whether such raw materials are to be subjected to decontamination procedures during the course of processing. But, in the absence of a continuing environmental surveillance program, finished-product control is a perfunctory exercise.

FINISHED-PRODUCT CONTROL

It can be argued that the product offered for sale is the finished product and that it is therefore necessary to carry out routine salmonella analysis on the finished packaged products. The concept of finished-product analysis seems to be tightly held by both quality-control and regulatory workers, and there is a growing tendency in industry to demand that the finished product be analyzed and found free of salmonellae before it moves in commerce. Thus, finished products are sampled and assayed as a means of determining the success of in-process control, including raw-material inspection and environmental surveillance. A continuing microbiological audit of finished product is supplemental to, but should not replace, in-process control. The level or intensity of final-product examination should be adjusted in accordance with the results obtained on in-process samples. Thus, if environmental testing indicates the prescence of salmonellae, or if process control results indicate processing failure, then intensive analysis of the finished product must be undertaken.

Finished-product control demands a realistic and meaningful system for lotting the final product. The key to lot identification is homogeneity. A variety of factors are employed in setting the limits that define a lot of finished goods, e.g., the time period, raw materials used, the team of operating personnel, the process equipment line, the type of package, and the accessibility for sampling and testing.

A factor used with increasing frequency in this era of continuous production is the time period. The period employed can be quite flexible, but it is generally recommended that it not exceed 24 hours. Frequently, the time is much shorter than this; on high-speed lines it may, although rarely, be as short as 30 min. Limitation by shift is frequently used along with the other factors. The major objective is to adopt those limitations that maximize the probability that the lot is homogeneous.

When it is possible that a lot might be rejected, it becomes a matter of simple economics to make the lot as small as feasible. On the other hand, making the lot sizes smaller greatly increases the cost of sampling and analysis. As a consequence, the manufacturer is well advised to maintain in-process quality assurance procedures so that his lot size can be made as large and as uniform as possible with minimal risk of rejection.

The separate units of a given lot should be identified so that they can be distinguished from units of other lots. The marking or identification may be as simple as a date stamp on the container or as complex as an embossed code that has been derived from a table of random numbers. Anything is satisfactory that permits the manufacturer unequivocally to distinguish individual lots.

It is sometimes convenient to divide an original lot into one or more sublots for retest purposes. This is facilitated if the original numbering of the cases or packages has been sequential. Such coding is sometimes particularly useful when it is desired to separate the start-up segment of the lot from the middle or end segments.

In summary, for purposes of retest or recheck as described in this report, a lot consists of: (1) an identifiable and identified unit of production, distinguishable from other units, that has been packaged (bagged, containerized, etc.) (2) within a determined period of time (3) without major interruptions of flow, shutdowns, or other changes (such as the use of different sources of raw materials) that could be expected to cause one portion of the lot to differ significantly in integrity from another and that is (4) complete and (5) accessible for inspection and testing.

By definition, a representative lot sample is a small-scale replica of the lot itself from which one or more smaller test samples may be drawn for assay. The difficulty of assuring that the representative sample is a faithful replica of the lot in question is well recognized. There is no recourse except to employ as much ingenuity as possible.

When a lot is to be tested, all the components must be located and assembled. A sampling plan is then adopted and applied in a statistically random manner. One commonly used plan is the so-called square-root procedure, i.e., the number of samples drawn is equal to the square root of the number of packages in the lot. In some instances, this number becomes unreasonably large and accordingly is limited—to 10 percent when the lot contains more than 100 cases or packages and to still lower percentages in larger lot sizes. In other cases, the square root may be considered too small a number, especially if the product is in relatively large packages. In these cases, one draws a sample from each package. On statistical grounds, the square-root plan is simply a practical rule-of-thumb guide.

To avoid bias, the components of the representative sample should be taken in a random fashion. Depending on the number and size of the test samples required, they may be obtained directly from the array of material called the representative sample, or the representative sample may be blended or mixed to give a composite replica of the original lot. The choice depends on the normal distribution of the food or food material. For a food that is consumed package by package, blending or mixing is inapplicable. If the lot is a food ingredient or raw material intended for further processing in which it will be blended and mixed with other ingredients, it may be wise to mix and blend the representative sample.

Whatever method is employed, test samples should be drawn randomly. The number of test samples required is determined by the confidence or probability limits that one wishes to establish.

A serious impediment to the establishment of effective industry quality-control programs has been the so-called "zero tolerance" for *Salmonella*. The term is usually interpreted to mean that no bacteria of the genus *Salmonella* may be present in a food product, that the presence of *Salmonella* is violative, regardless of the level of contamination. This interpretation of the zero tolerance does not take into consideration the nature of the food product or the use to which it is to be put. It does not define the nature of the lot, the numbers of samples to be examined, or their size.

It is not now apparent whether the zero-tolerance concept evolved directly from the pronouncements of the U.S. Food and Drug Administration or if the punitive actions of FDA led industry to make this interpretation. In any event, in the absence of fixed guidelines this general interpretation has become established. Section 402 of the U.S. Food, Drug, and Cosmetic Act of 1938 states: "A food shall be deemed to be adulterated—(a) (1) if it bears or contains any poisonous or deleterious substance which may render it injurious to health." Lack of quantitative information relative to infectivity of salmonellae and host susceptibility has led to a rigid interpretation of this clause in the Act, i.e., that any salmonellae whatever, however few, are considered injurious to health. This interpretation ignores the second part of the provision relating to adulterated food, which reads "but in case the substance is not an added substance such food shall not be considered adulterated under this clause if the quantity of such substance in such food does not ordinarily render it injurious to health. . . ." Thus, the absence of knowledge with respect to infectivity and susceptibility has led to acceptance of the first clause in the section and rejection of the second, and, thus, to the zero-tolerance terminology.

The absence of quantitative guidelines has hindered the establishment of industry control programs. Since statistical quality control embodies conscious admission that a finite incidence of "defects" may occur, it is incompatible with the usual interpretation of the zero tolerance. It would be a step forward to publish quantitative guidelines that could serve as a basis for the establishment of meaningful control programs. Such guidelines should take into account a number of factors.

THE ULTIMATE MANNER IN WHICH THE FOOD IS TO BE USED

If it is a consumer product, does its usage involve cooking or some other culinary treatment that would result in salmonella destruction? If the material is an ingredient to be used in the formulation of some other product, do the manufacturing procedures result in the elimination of salmonellae? Obviously, the food or ingredient that will ultimately be used under conditions resulting in salmonella destruction is far less hazardous than one that will be consumed without such decontamination, and the quantitative guidelines should take this into account. This does not ignore the danger of bringing a contaminated food into the kitchen or processing area but does recognize that the level of risk entailed is influenced by ultimate usage.

THE ABUSE POTENTIAL OF THE PRODUCT

Although relatively little is known about infectivity, it is axiomatic that the likelihood of infection is directly related to dosage. Thus, if a product is one that will permit the growth of salmonellae when exposed to temperatures within the growth range, such a product carries with it far greater risk than one so constituted as to be inhibitory to salmonella development. Thus, one must look upon fluid egg products as a greater risk than dried egg products. And candy containing little moisture would be even less hazardous than dried eggs, since the latter may well be abused when reconstituted. The likelihood of abuse must also be considered. Thus, it is unlikely that ice cream would be abused to the extent that salmonella growth would occur, since under such conditions the product would completely lose its character. On the other hand, frozen cream-filled pastries might, in some instances, be mishandled to an extent permitting extensive salmonella growth and yet retain their basic character.

SENSITIVE INGREDIENTS

Some ingredients of foods have historically been considered potential sources of salmonellae in finished products. Examples are egg products, dried milk, dry inactive yeast, coconut, unroasted nutmeats, and gums. The list of "sensitive" ingredients will undoubtedly become longer as investigation increases knowledge of the distribution of salmonellae. For example, a few years ago no one would have thought to consider carmine red dye a critical ingredient, but it is now well known that widespread contamination of food products did occur as a result of the distribution of at least one lot of dye that was heavily contaminated with salmonellae. A product containing one or more "sensitive" ingredients is potentially a greater risk than one not containing such ingredients.

POPULATION AT RISK

If the population normally using the product is one known to be of high susceptibility to salmonella infection, then the utmost quality control should be exercised. Included in this category would be powdered prepared infant formulas, dry infant food, therapeutic diet supplements, geriatric foods, and drugs.

CLASSIFICATION OF FOOD PRODUCTS
ACCORDING TO RISK

At this point, a system of food-product classification on the basis of potential health hazard is suggested, based on consideration of three product characteristics:

A. *The product contains an ingredient that has been identified as a significant potential factor in salmonellosis.*

B. *The manufacturing process does not include a controlled step that would destroy salmonellae.* The processing step referred to here can be heat, concentration, pH change, or other change in physical or chemical characteristics known to destroy salmonellae. For brevity in further discussion, this characteristic will be referred to as "contains no final pasteurizing step."

C. *There is a substantial likelihood of microbiological growth if mishandled or "abused" in distribution or consumer usage.* The principal criterion is whether the food product is a good medium for salmonella growth, either as it is distributed in food channels or as it is normally prepared for consumer use.

If we consider a food product as incorporating any or all of these hazard characteristics, we can develop a "shorthand" description of the product as in these examples:

A B C meaning
    Contains a sensitive ingredient
    Has no "final pasteurizing" step
    Abuse potential is present
Or, O B O meaning
    No sensitive ingredient
    No "final pasteurizing" step
    No abuse potential

The letter indicates that the hazard characteristic is present; the use of "O" in the index position indicates that the hazard characteristic is not present.

The three general food hazard characteristics can be combined into eight configurations or permutations and can be ranked according to their potential consumer hazard.

In a special category, designated Category I, are placed food products intended for use by infants, the aged, and the infirm—the restricted population of high risk.

Category II—processed foods in this category are subject to all three of the general hazard characteristics (A B C). Examples of consumer products in this category are instantized dried milk and egg custard mix.

Category III—includes those products subject to two of the three general hazard considerations.

- A O C—the products of this type, e.g., custard-filled bakery goods or frozen precooked meals, are included in this category because of the use of "sensitive" ingredients and the abuse potential, but are subject to a pasteurizing step.
- A B O—these products contain a "sensitive" ingredient, have no "pasteurizing" step but have little or no abuse potential; the product as distributed or consumed does not support the growth of salmonellae. Examples are cake mixes, breakfast cocoa, and chocolate candy.
- O B C—no "sensitive" ingredient is included, but there is no "pasteurizing" step, and the product is subject to abuse. Products in this category include certain dry gravy and sauce mixes that do not include a sensitive ingredient.

Category IV—this category includes those products of relatively minor microbiological health hazard level. These foods are subject to only one of the general hazard characteristics.

- A O O—products that contain a "sensitive" ingredient, include a "pasteurizing" step, and offer no abuse potential. Examples include retail baked cakes and candies such as caramels.
- O B O—these products contain no "sensitive" ingredient, include no "pasteurizing" step, and have no abuse potential. Examples include "cold" processed confections and some frosting mixes.
- O O C—these products contain no "sensitive" ingredients, are "pasteurized," but are subject to potential abuse. Products of this type would be unusual, but a possible example is dry white-sauce mix.

Category V—foods in this category are subject to none of the microbiological hazard characteristics (O O O), and consequently they are of minimal hazard potential. The product contains no "sensitive" ingredient, is "pasteurized," and offers no abuse potential, for example, hard candy. Also included in this category are canned food products receiving sterilizing processes after packaging in the final container.

CLASSIFICATION OF FOOD INGREDIENTS

In the following listing of ingredient categories, roman numerals are again used. These correspond to the numerals used to classify finished product risks, although the criteria establishing risk are different. Since further processing of the raw materials is assumed, there are no Category I ingredients.

Category II—those ingredients designated as "sensitive" or containing sensitive ingredients as a part of the formulation.

Category III—compound ingredients not containing sensitive materials.

Category IV—ingredients of organic origin that historically have not been implicated as sources of salmonella contamination. Modified starches constitute an example.

Category V—food ingredients in this category are inorganic materials and those organic substances that, as a result of their processing or physicochemical properties, have been shown to destroy salmonellae effectively. Included in this category are leavening acid, salt, sodium bicarbonate, sugar, citric acid, and vinegar.

In summary, processed foods and food ingredients arranged according to the five categories mentioned are at the same time arranged in relation to their potential hazard. A food manufacturer using this classification system is able to identify his products with appropriate emphasis for routine control, audit, and testing. Similarly, these categories form the basis for a program for levels of microbiological testing that can be applied in the event that there is reason to believe that a product could have been contaminated with salmonellae.

DESIGNING THE CONTROL PROGRAM

In any given processing facility, the control program must be designed to meet the specialized requirements of the operation. In some cases, this will involve greatest emphasis on inspection of raw material; in others, on specific processing steps; while in still others, the point of greatest emphasis may appropriately be in the examination of finished product.

The matter of salmonella control is complicated by the question of distribution of salmonellae when they do occur in a food product. If this defect is random, it is not controlled by time; i.e., there is an equal opportunity for contamination to occur at any stage of the operation. If, on the other hand, contamination was limited to a certain segment of time during processing, then the defect would not be randomly distributed throughout the lot. If distribution is random, regular sampling procedures will detect the organism; if nonrandom, there is virtually no assurance of control unless the regulatory nature of time is known.

As previously indicated, in sampling a production lot, random sampling is recommended. A random sample is one in which any inidividual tested is as likely to detect contamination as any other. This does not mean that one sample at one given time gives a measure of control of finished product, but rather that selecting samples at random during processing gives information on the lot. It is important that the lot be so defined that the foregoing requirements are met.

Inasmuch as salmonella contamination of foods produced in conformance with good practice and subjected to well-designed controls will be at a low level, if it occurs at all, the most practical method of testing a questioned lot is by attribute sampling. In attribute sampling, the lot is considered to be made up of a large number of 25-g units, and the lot is accepted or rejected on the basis of the maximum proportion of defective (salmonella positive) units that the lot can be presumed, with 95 percent confidence, to contain. Basic to such a program is the requirement that the units selected for testing be representative of the lot under scrutiny (see above). Under such conditions, if it can be demonstrated that the lot in question contains fewer than 5 percent positive units, it may be concluded that the average level of contamination of the lot is less than 5 organisms in 2,500 g, or less than 1 organism in 500 g.*

If the average proportion of salmonella-positive units in a lot is denoted by y, the probability (P) of having one or more defective units in a group of n units is given by

$$P = 1 - 10^{-0.433ny}. \tag{1}$$

The probability that there will be no defective units in a group of n units is

$$Q = (1 - P) = 10^{-0.433ny}, \tag{2}$$

which can be rearranged to

$$n = (-2.303/y) \log (1 - P). \tag{3}$$

This gives the number of units (n) that, if examined and found to be all negative, will give assurance P that the proportion of positive units in the lot averages less than y. For example, if 60 representative units are tested and no positives found, the probability is 95 percent that if the sampling and testing were extended indefinitely the positive units found would not exceed 5 percent, equivalent to a lot average of fewer than one organism in 500 g. The same experimental result gives 99 percent prob-

---

* It must be remembered that if the testing is done by variable sampling rather than by attribute sampling, such conclusions might not be warranted.

ability that the lot contains fewer than 7 percent positive units (lot average of less than one organism in 380 g), and 91 percent probability that the lot contains fewer than 4 percent positive units (lot average fewer than one organism in 625 g).

It is to be noted that if all units are negative, increasing the number of units tested beyond 60 yields additional meaningful information hardly commensurate with the effort expended. Thus, 90 units tested and found all negative would give 95 percent probability that 3 percent or less of the units in the lot might be positive (a maximum lot average of one organism in 830 g). It is difficult to believe that the probabilities established for the lot by testing 90 units differ enough from those based on 60 units to have public health significance.

This analysis is displayed in graphic fashion in Figure 12, in which the maximum proportion of the units of a lot that can be assumed to be negative, with a 95 percent probability of being correct, is plotted against the number of units actually tested and found negative.

The fundamental relationships expressed in Equations (2) and (3) above, may be employed to compute the probabilities associated with all possible results obtained from testing any number of units, and tabula-

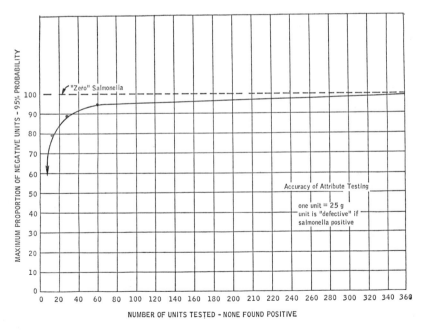

FIGURE 12 Accuracy of attribute testing.

tions of the resulting computations are available. One such is "Accuracy of Attribute Sampling," published by the Consumer and Marketing Service, USDA (March 1966).

CRITERIA FOR ACCEPTANCE

Under the best of circumstances the processor's routine surveillance will from time to time raise questions of whether a particular lot or sublot of product should be rejected. This situation may arise from a variety of causes: suspected malfunction of equipment in a critical process step, evidence of inadequate sanitizing procedures prior to startup, use of raw material that had not been properly cleared by quality control, the finding of salmonellae in environmental sampling, or the isolation of salmonellae from a routine finished-product sample. Any of these circumstances, as well as others that could be defined, makes it necessary to consider carefully the acceptability of the finished product. If there is evidence that the finished product may contain salmonellae, then a decision must be made about whether the product is adulterated within the meaning of the federal Food, Drug, and Cosmetic Act. This assessment demands a quantitative determination of the status of salmonellae within the questioned lot.

The following criteria are proposed for acceptance of questioned food lots in the various categories defined in the immediately preceding section of this report:

Category I—60 units (25 g each) tested and found negative. As noted above, this gives a 95 percent probability that there is one organism or fewer in any 500 g of the lot in question.

Category II—29 units (25 g each) tested and found negative; 95 percent probability that there is one organism or fewer in 250 g.

Category III—13 units (25 g each) tested and found negative; 95 percent probability that there is one organism or fewer in 125 g.

Category IV—same as Category III.

Category V—not ordinarily subject to salmonella contamination, but if required, test as for Category III.

The criteria proposed for Categories IV and V are identical with those for Category III, because tests of fewer than 13 units will not establish an estimate with 95 percent assurance.

Obviously, the fulfillment of the acceptance criteria proposed above entails the analysis of large numbers of 25-g units. It would be advantageous if it were possible to reduce the labor and cost of testing by pooling samples. Such pooling could be justified only if it were established that the sensitivity of the test procedure was not thereby diminished. This would be true only if all tests were negative and the required total number of test units had been examined, viz., 1,500 g for Category I, 725 g for Category II, and 325 g for Categories III, IV, and V.

The validity of pooling rests on the requirement that the sensitivity of the test procedure not be diminished, and there is but little information available with respect to the actual sensitivities of the various procedures routinely used for detecting salmonellae in foods and other products. The methodologies applied have, for the most part, evolved empirically, and "improved procedures" have been judged to be so on the basis of improved recovery. Quantitative data on true sensitivities are lacking, particularly with respect to the effectiveness of various procedures in the recovery of *naturally occurring* salmonellae.

In the analysis of most foods and drugs, the "preferred" procedures now involve pre-enrichment of the sample prior to subculture in selective media. Empirically, the ratio of food sample to pre-enrichment medium is 10 percent (w/v). A decade or so ago this involved examination of 10 g of dried egg solids in 100 ml of lactose broth. Subsequently, when it was recognized that animal feed ingredients constitute a salmonella problem, procedures were evolved for their analyses. In this case, larger samples were examined, e.g., 25 g of sample was enriched in 250 ml of lactose broth. When salmonellae were encountered in dried milk, yet another "standard procedure," entailing the reconstitution of 100 g of sample in 1,000 ml of sterile water was developed. Similarily, the recognition that chocolate may be contaminated with salmonellae led to the establishment of a "standard procedure," the enrichment of 100 g of candy in 1,000 ml of sterilized reconstituted nonfat dry milk. Thus, the size of the sample being examined was gradually increased but without consideration of the influence of sample size on sensitivity.

The influence of sample size on the sensitivity of recovery procedures is of considerable importance to industry. The larger the sample examined, the less the cost of the control program. Or, alternatively, if larger samples can be analyzed without significant reduction in sensitivity, then greater degrees of confidence in control procedures can be realized at no added cost.

Unfortunately, there is a dearth of information with respect to the influence of sample size on sensitivity. However, there has been a trend in industry laboratories toward the analysis of larger samples than are prescribed by "standard procedures." For example, in a number of laboratories, 400 g of sample is enriched in 4,000 ml of enriched medium. Recently, a study was conducted wherein the effectiveness of analyzing composite 400-g samples of dried egg products was compared with that of analyzing multiple 25-g samples from the same lots of material. The detailed results of this study, reported in Appendix C, indicate that some sensitivity is sacrificed in the analysis of 400-g composite samples, and that, on the average, approximately six salmonellae had to be contained in the 400-g sample if its analysis were to yield positive results. This assumes that the analysis of a 25-sample, containing a single salmonella, would yield positive findings.

The decreased sensitivity resulting from the analysis of 400-g samples, as compared with the testing of multiple 25-g units, does not negate the value of examining large samples. In a food product with a low level of salmonella contamination, the chances of detecting the organism in a single 400-g sample are manifestly greater than in a single 25-g sample, even though the *sensitivity* of the test involving a 25-g sample is apparently more than twice as great. No doubt the influence of sample size on sensitivity varies greatly, depending on the material under investigation. The cost saving, or increased reliability, that accrues to the analysis of larger samples warrants investigations of this type on individual products subject to salmonella control.

Yet another approach to reducing analytical costs is "wet compositing." This involves the subculture of multiple pre-enrichment units into a single tube of selective broth. Thus, multiple "standard" sized units are pre-enriched, but the pre-enrichment cultures are pooled for selective culturing. Appendix D presents the results of a recent study on the evaluation of this method. It will be noted that results from "wet compositing" generally agree well with the results that would be predicted from the analysis of the individual components. In the study of 106 different "wet composites," the results were in disagreement only eight times. In seven instances, the "wet composite" was found negative for salmonellae, whereas one or more of the individual components was positive. Interestingly, in one case the composite was positive although each of its ten components was negative. This procedure appears to offer yet another approach to the reduction in cost and to permit the achievement of higher levels of confidence in control procedures.

If, in testing the indicated number of units drawn from a lot in question, a single positive test is obtained, several interpretations are possible.

• The lot may in fact be contaminated to an extent that is unacceptable.

• The lot may in fact be acceptable, the positive test representing a chance occurrence within the acceptable probability limits established for the lot in question.

• The lot may in fact be acceptable, the positive test being the result of contamination in drawing the sample or contamination in the testing laboratory.

To determine which of these possibilities pertains, additional units may be tested in accordance with the USDA tables mentioned earlier, since these show that:

Category I—60 units tested, all negative, is equivalent to 92 units tested with 91 negative and 1 positive.

Category II—29 units tested, all negative, is equivalent to 48 units tested with 47 negative and 1 positive.

Category III—13 units, all negative, is equivalent to 22 units with 21 negative and 1 positive.

It is therefore proposed that to avoid rejection on the basis of a *single* positive test, the indicated number of additional units be tested, and if *all are negative,* that the questioned lot be judged acceptable.

The finding of more than a single positive in any series of tested units as described above is a basis for rejection of the questioned lot.

If there is good evidence that contamination has occurred in the drawing of the samples or in the laboratory, it would seem reasonable to retest the lot after these errors have been corrected. What to do with unacceptable lots will vary with the individual situation, e.g.:

● Certain products can be reprocessed to destroy viable salmonellae.

● The lot may be directed to another process in which there is a step effective in destroying viable salmonellae.

● The lot may be destroyed.

If a positive result is obtained in a pooled portion testing program, its significance cannot be readily established with the desired assurance except by further testing. In this case, the testing program should be repeated with representative samples using the full recommended number of 25-g test units, and unless all are negative the lot should be rejected.

Table 8 summarizes the proposed acceptance criteria.

TABLE 8   Acceptance Criteria

Product Category	Number of Units Tested with No Positives	Number of Units Tested with No More than One Positive	Significance[a] 95% Probability of One Organism or Less in
I	60 (1,500 g)	92 (2,300 g)	500 g
II	29 (725 g)	48 (1,200 g)	250 g
III	13 (325 g)	22 (550 g)	125 g
IV	13 (325 g)	22 (550 g)	125 g
V[b]	13 (325 g)	22 (550 g)	125 g

[a] Accuracy of Attribute Sampling, USDA Consumer and Marketing Service, March 1966.
[b] Not normally applicable.

In summary, the laboratory must play a key role in the control of salmonellae. The nature of the control program will vary from industry to industry, product to product, and plant to plant, and in a given operation the points of emphasis may vary from time to time.

Environmental surveillance is the backbone of effective control. Without it, the significance of finished-product control is greatly compromised. In products the manufacture of which does not involve decontamination steps, greatest emphasis must be placed upon raw-material inspection.

Acceptance criteria, based on attribute sampling, are suggested. These take into account categories of risk, based on product characteristics and usage. It is felt that adoption of these criteria will be a forward step toward the establishment of improved industry control over the salmonella defect.

11 Regulatory Controls

The U.S. Department of Agriculture and the Food and Drug Administration are the agencies primarily responsible for regulatory action concerning foods and feeds that move in interstate commerce. The Department of the Interior also gives some attention to salmonella, and the U.S. Public Health Service, although having no regulatory jurisdiction, contributes importantly by preparing model ordinances and codes, by advising on inspection and control procedures, by epidemiological investigation and surveillance, and by training in laboratory procedures used in salmonella control. State and municipal agencies are responsible for local and intrastate regulatory actions insofar as they are carried out.

The USDA functions as a regulatory agency in the control of salmonellosis by authority of numerous laws and regulations. Under this authority it: (1) inspects meats for wholesomeness and can restrict the use of contaminated meats, meat products, and nonmeat products intended for use in meats; (2) inspects poultry processing plants and inspects and grades eggs, egg products, and poultry; (3) administers the National Poultry and Turkey Improvement Plans in cooperation with state agencies; (4) controls the introduction of infectious, contagious, or communicable diseases of animals into the United States from foreign countries by means of animals or animal products or in feed and feed ingredients; (5) safeguards veterinary biologics; and (6) inspects and grades dairy products.

Of the foregoing activities, only the National Poultry and Turkey Improvement Programs were directed originally toward salmonella control, and even these were designed as animal health measures, not to protect man against infection. With the current interest in salmonellosis, how-

157

ever, certain USDA programs have been expanded to include salmonella control:

● Dry milk, processed egg, and rendered animal by-product manufacturing plants under USDA inspection are examined periodically, and their products are tested for salmonellae.

● A program has been announced (and presumably will be activated) whereby manufacturers will be asked to recall "ready-to-eat" and "warm-and-eat" meat and poultry products found to contain salmonellae. Furthermore, fresh meats and poultry slaughtered in USDA-inspected plants will be retained if found to be "heavily contaminated" with salmonellae.

● The National Turkey Improvement Plan provides for the control of serotype Typhimurium in turkeys.

● The veterinary biologics program includes measures to assure freedom from salmonellae in veterinary biological products.

● Research and education in support of salmonella control programs have been expanded.

The Food, Drug, and Cosmetic Act and regulations for its administration provide the authority for the FDA's activities in regulatory control of salmonellosis. One aspect of the FDA's responsibility for safeguarding public health is the protection of the consumer from hazardous foods and drugs moving in interstate commerce. The agency discharges this responsibility by promulgating regulations and guidelines for industry and by plant inspections, surveillance of products, recall of suspected products from the market, and where deemed necessary, court action against products or manufacturers.

Historically, the FDA has focused its attention primarily on products involved in outbreaks of salmonellosis and on foods known frequently to carry salmonellae. Prior to March 1966, the FDA's planned control program covered (1) eggs and egg products, (2) dried yeast, and (3) imported coconut. Subsequently, programs were developed for (4) nonfat dry milk, (5) thyroid and other drug products of animal origin, and (6) rendered animal by-products used in food. More recently, although its primary concern has continued to be with products associated with disease, the FDA has examined a wide variety of foods and ingredients not known to be involved in human salmonellosis, on the basis that the presence of salmonellae poses a potential hazard in any food, and that the presence of these organisms, in any numbers, causes the food to be adulterated in terms of the Food, Drug, and Cosmetic Act.

Along with product surveillance, the FDA has greatly increased its educational activities for the benefit of food and feed producers.

The U.S. Department of the Interior has microbiological control responsibilities through the Bureau of Commercial Fisheries and through the Water Pollution Control Administration. In addition, the Interstate Commerce Commission, through its regulation of interstate transport by rail, highways, and air, contributes to prevention of salmonellosis.

With rare exception, the inspection and control of food-service activities falls within the jurisdiction of state and local agencies. State agencies, usually the Department of Agriculture, also may inspect food- and feed-manufacturing plants operating within state boundaries and may examine products shipped into their states from outside. The effectiveness of inspection and the interest in salmonella control varies widely.

EFFECTIVENESS OF SALMONELLA CONTROL BY REGULATORY AGENCIES

When the U.S. Department of Agriculture adopted the National Poultry Improvement Plan, serological tests indicated that there was an incidence of serotype Pullorum of about 1 in 25 breeder birds; today only 1 in 22,700 gives a positive test. Similarly, in 1944, the year the National Turkey Improvement Plan was adopted, the incidence in breeder turkeys was about 1 in 50; now fewer than 1 in 44,000 react (from *Destruction of Salmonellae.* A report of the Western Experiment Station Collaborators Conference held in Albany, California, p. 117). Serotype Pullorum and serotype Gallinarum have decreased in importance to the point that neither is among the first ten isolates from poultry.

From the standpoint of public health, this record is not of great significance, although it is very important in poultry production. Pullorum disease is transmissible to man, but such transmission is primarily industry-related and not a public health issue. Fowl typhoid apparently is not communicable to man.

The effectiveness of specific control programs of the USDA and the FDA for salmonella contamination in foods and feeds can not be satisfactorily assessed since there is no useful baseline of incidence of salmonellosis in man from which to measure change. In addition, except for control in egg products, specific programs have probably not been in operation long enough to be reflected in national statistics. It can fairly be assumed, however, that the processing surveillance programs developed for control of salmonella contamination of egg products, nonfat dried milk, and other foods have reduced the level of contamination and thus probably of salmonellosis in man. Vigorous control of contamination of animal feeds has only just begun and can not yet have had significant effect on either animal or human salmonellosis.

Much of the salmonellosis in man is, in any case, not related to foods subject to these specific control programs but results from mishandling of contaminated raw foods or of processed foods at the level of preparation for consumption. Regulatory control at this level pertains to mass-feeding facilities, and there is no way of judging its effectiveness. There is, of course, no regulatory control of home-prepared meals.

IMPROVEMENT OF REGULATORY CONTROL

The independence of the several federal, state, and local agencies has enabled them to attack the over-all problem from different viewpoints, yet some weaknesses remain because their programs are uncoordinated. It is important that governmental actions be consistent and uniform, and that they be understood by the segment of industry that is affected.

The FDA, the USDA, and, at times, local agencies may all be concerned in control of food products from a plant, and all may conduct surveillance. An obvious industry-wide example is the surveillance by both the FDA and the USDA of egg pasteurization plants. Development and use by all inspection agencies of common inspection protocols and methods and the availability of properly trained inspection personnel would permit one agency to be delegated the task of inspecting for all. For example, if USDA inspection is required in a plant for any reason, its inspectors could be authorized to conduct any inspection required by the FDA or state agencies. Similarly, state inspectors could be delegated to act simultaneously for the state, the FDA, and the USDA, or FDA inspectors for the USDA and state agencies. Public funds and personnel time would be saved without diminishing consumer protection, and industry would be saved the inconvenience and lost time caused by multiple inspections.

Regulatory programs aimed at preventing human salmonellosis should be planned, particularly in light of the limited personnel available, to concentrate on those foods and products of highest risk. A scheme for estimating risk is presented in Chapter 10.

There is some concern that economic and personnel limitations may dictate that the largest producers of products subject to regulatory control are given disproportionately great attention in routine surveillance. Any such tendency, whether in federal, state, or local activities, should be avoided, for the product of a small producer can be as hazardous as that of a giant corporation.

Food-service operations are, in general, subject to regulatory control only by local authorities. These operations (restaurants, catering services, school lunchrooms, hospitals, nursing homes, and the like) are frequently the sources of outbreaks of salmonellosis, and the quality of their services is likely to be improved only if regulatory control is improved. The U.S. Public Health Service and other agencies have provided guidelines for control. They should be evaluated and, if adopted, enforced.

12 Surveillance

PURPOSE

Surveillance is the ongoing scrutiny of the occurrence, distribution, and trends of a disease by means of systematic collection, consolidation, and evaluation of all available data, including initiation of the necessary investigations as indicated by analysis of these data. The goal of surveillance in the present instance is the control and ultimate prevention of salmonellosis.

Because of the widespread distribution of salmonellosis throughout the country, the interstate aspects of its transmission, the many complex interrelationships in the total ecological picture of salmonellosis, and the multiple resources available, effective surveillance can best be conducted by a national agency such as the U.S. Public Health Service, but only if there is effective and active support by state and local health authorities.

National surveillance implies activities on a national level, but in practice the surveillance program must be vigorously supported and promoted on a state and community level if it is to be a truly effective guide to the control and prevention program. Furthermore, support must be forthcoming from private physicians, laboratories, city and county health departments, and individual and collective members of both manufacturing and nonmanufacturing industries.

A problem must be defined before it can be brought under control, and definition depends on notification of all cases and isolations. Reports of large epidemics, whether interstate or intrastate, will ultimately come directly or indirectly to the attention of public health officials. Of even greater importance are the small outbreaks and the individual isolated cases that occur but that, unless cultured, are not reported. It has been shown in the National Salmonella Surveillance Program that isolated reports of salmonellosis are almost always associated with additional, related cases that are uncovered during investigations. Accordingly, as the individual cases are reported and investigations initiated, the total picture of salmonellosis becomes better defined.

The effectiveness of surveillance becomes apparent through a decrease in the incidence of disease. Although national statistics do not indicate a reduction of salmonellosis (other than typhoid fever) in recent years, there is reason to believe that dissemination of salmonellae through food and other commercial vehicles has been reduced. The associated decrease in incidence of salmonellosis that would be expected to be observed apparently has been masked by the increased efficiency of uncovering and reporting cases.

Several examples of how surveillance has produced data indicating an unusual situation may be illustrative of the benefits of surveillance. There are, for example, instances in which increased incidence of a certain serotype or identification of unusual serotypes was noted in the surveillance program, appropriate investigations were conducted, and subsequently, control was initiated. Thus, the serotype Derby episode in 1963 was initially uncovered through surveillance. When the first unusual isolations of Derby serotypes were noted in the weekly reports, an investigation indicated the hospital-related nature of the initial cases and alerted the investigators to subsequent isolations. Studies then identified the vehicle of infection, raw eggs, which allowed control measures to be instituted, though it was months before the epidemic was actually brought under adequate control and the number of isolations of serotype Derby decreased.

In a second example, increase in the number of isolations of serotype Typhimurium in a northwestern city was detected because surveillance had been in progress for a number of years. When approximately 10 isolations of serotype Typhimurium were identified within one week, a number that was distinctly above normal, appropriate investigations were conducted. This led to the definition of a situation in which commercially prepared meringue pies were shown to be the vehicle of infection, the distribution of reported cases throughout the city, county, and state paralleling the distribution of the vehicle.

These episodes represent large epidemics, the investigation of which identified the vehicle of infection and thus probably prevented additional cases. Other epidemiological investigation of explosive, common source epidemics might identify the vehicle only after the explosion is over.

Even so, the data should be of assistance in preventing further cases arising from the same circumstances. For example, investigation of the large outbreak of serotype Typhimurium gastroenteritis traced to contaminated turkey rolls in Oxford, Nebraska, in 1967 did not reduce the number of cases in that episode but will be important in reducing the possibility of similar outbreaks in the future.

Surveillance methods should encompass all potential sources of information concerning salmonellosis. Since salmonellosis can not be clinically differentiated from other diarrheal diseases, effective reporting can only be based on laboratory identification of the organism. An exception arises when epidemiological investigations reveal multiple cases, obviously related to a common source, but when only one or a few patients are actually cultured and found to be infected with salmonellae. In this instance, all epidemiologically related cases should be reported. This is especially true of family outbreaks.

This limitation in reporting leads to significant underreporting and makes surveillance more difficult. Additionally, the low reported mortality and the natural reluctance to report "minor" diseases aggravate the difficulty.

At present, the surveillance program of the National Communicable Disease Center (NCDC) depends mainly on weekly reports submitted from each state laboratory (and the New York City public health laboratory and Beth Israel Salmonella Reference Laboratory) that list all salmonella isolates from human and nonhuman sources identified in their laboratories. Multiple isolations of the same serotype from the same patient are excluded. Additionally, the state animal diagnostic laboratories submit reports, as do the Food and Drug Administration from its product-surveillance activities and the Department of Agriculture from its reference laboratories. Occasional reports are received from private industry, and there are undoubtedly many isolations identified at least as to genus in hospital, city, and private laboratories that are never reported to the state laboratories and thus not to the NCDC.

Additionally, reports of investigations of epidemics are received from state and city health departments, the FDA, and the USDA; and occasionally outbreaks are uncovered through public news media.

As these data are received, they are analyzed for unusual characteristics, such as increased incidence of a single serotype, unusual concentration of one or more serotypes in a geographic area, or an unusual association, such as serotype Dublin from a human being.

Rare serotypes can serve as epidemiological markers, allowing accurate delineation of the spread of infection, and potentially, the source of infection. Another device is phage typing, which at present is only available for further differentiating *S. typhi* and serotype Typhimurium.

Investigations are ordinarily initiated by contacting the involved state public health department, discussing the data, and, as appropriate, offering assistance for investigations. The FDA and the USDA may be notified of unusual findings, and cooperative studies may be initiated.

A monthly surveillance report is prepared summarizing the data after they have been analyzed, and comparisons are made with previous data. In addition to reviewing these data, the monthly report serves to call attention to potential or actual outbreaks, to educate public health and private individuals about the current situation, to report investigations in both the field and laboratory, and to stimulate more concerted efforts toward control and prevention.

Surveillance extends also to nonhuman sources. Isolations from animals are carefully followed, and appropriate investigations initiated. Isolations reported by the FDA and by the USDA are compared with other nonhuman and human isolations to see whether there are any indications of common-source outbreaks.

The FDA maintains surveillance of potentially contaminated foods and other products. The routine weekly reports reflect the FDA's surveillance of products previously associated with salmonellae. Specimens for laboratory examination are also obtained during the FDA's routine inspection of certain industries, and whenever an outbreak is associated with a commercial product that is in the FDA's jurisdiction, an investigation is promptly instituted.

The USDA maintains surveillance over the production of milk, meats, and related products. Its reports of isolations reflect its routine and investigative activities.

The NCDC usually cultures samples from nonhuman sources only as part of epidemic or field investigative activities. Occasionally, following a lead from the FDA or the USDA, the NCDC initiates product surveillance.

It is recognized that the current surveillance program is not totally inclusive. Since surveillance is dependent on laboratory identification of an organism, the laboratory facilities available need to be expanded to encourage the collection of stool specimens from more individuals with diarrheal disease. Also, the quality of the laboratory work needs to be upgraded. Additional local laboratories available for the routine culturing of all diarrheal disease are needed in hospitals and cities and organisms identified as salmonellae should be referred to the state laboratory for serotyping. Resources should be made available to states and possibly counties and cities for additional laboratory, epidemiological, veterinary, statistical, and clerical assistance so that more investigations can be conducted at the local level.

The need to report all isolations of salmonellae from all levels to the appropriate public health authorities requires constant emphasis. Some city laboratories currently identify the genus *Salmonella* from fecal specimens but do not send the isolate to the state laboratory for further identification and do not report the isolation beyond their own departments.

Consideration should be given to maintaining some type of special surveillance over certain population groups, such as hospital personnel, employees in food-processing plants, and food handlers. There needs to be emphasis on physical examinations including appropriate cultures from employees returning to work in these industries after gastrointestinal disease.

Product surveillance has proved to be of value, especially when leads are developed from human and animal surveillance activities. An expansion in this area to include the routine laboratory examination of a variety of commercial products and of the physical environment of product plants should be promoted. Laboratory surveillance programs beginning with raw materials and extending to the final product would be established in industries suspected of distributing salmonella-contaminated products, industries suggested by epidemiological studies, and randomly selected industries. The FDA, the USDA, the NCDC, and private industry should be stimulated to expand their activities in this area, making available all reports to the NCDC as part of the ongoing surveillance activities.

Surveillance activities should attempt to define better the circumstances under which food becomes contaminated. The resulting data should be disseminated to all individuals to whom it would be useful through surveillance reports or other routine or spot publications, including industrial information media.

In an attempt to stimulate better reporting, pilot areas throughout the country should be selected and intensified surveillance activities initiated there with support from the Public Health Service. These intensive study areas could be selected after consultation with state public health agencies and private industry, an effort being made to develop improved methods of surveillance.

Since a number of countries throughout the world identify salmonella organisms and maintain surveillance, an attempt should be made to utilize international data in the surveillance program as an indicator of potential hazards related to imported foods, feeds, manufactured products, or personal travel. Domestic surveillance has demonstrated several times the importation of certain serotypes previously not frequently seen within the United States. For example, in 1962, public health authorities in Canada noted an increase in the incidence of serotype Thompson associated with human diarrhea. Investigations revealed a connection with a commercial cake mix product that was confirmed in the laboratory. The U.S. Public Health Service, with knowledge of the Canadian situation, was alert to the possibility of a similar situation in the United States which, however, did not occur.

Another example of benefits from international exchange of surveillance information comes from the outbreak of typhoid fever in Aberdeen, Scotland, in 1964, which was shown to be the result of the distribution of imported, contaminated corned beef. With this knowledge, the USDA was able to maintain tight surveillance over the importation of this product into the United States.

13   Education and Training for Prevention of Salmonellosis

A national program to minimize the occurrence of salmonellosis will require concerted action by many people and communications systems through which participants can be informed and motivated to take an active part within their respective spheres of interest. Available scientific evidence clearly indicates the need for establishing more effective multiple barriers to transmission of the salmonellae from the excreta of infected animals or human beings through environmental vehicles such as contaminated food, water, animal feeds, or medicinal products to other susceptible persons or animals. The rather common occurrence of salmonellae in the digestive tracts of different animal species, including man, and the persistence of these organisms for protracted periods outside the host under a variety of environmental conditions, make control of their dissemination very complex problems involving literally millions of people in nearly all walks of life. Practically speaking, salmonellae can not now be excluded from most raw foods, especially those of animal origin, and all persons who prepare foods at home or commercially should be educated to render these products safe before serving them to the consumer.

The U.S. food-service industries employ about 3.3 million persons in more than 370,000 restaurants, and they hire about 250,000 new employees annually.[1,2] According to the National Restaurant Association, the distribution of these employees by job categories is approximately as follows:

- Managerial, professional, or supervisory   20%
- Technical jobs involving special training   28%
  (e.g., bartenders, cooks, and bakers)
- Nontechnical jobs involving no special training
    (a) Waiters, counter help, kitchen helpers, etc.   46%
    (b) Clerical workers, hostesses, charwomen, etc.   6%

While the employees of the food-service industries represent only a small part (less than 25 percent) of the total audience that needs instruction and motivation, they well illustrate the variety of people with whom communication is desirable. Instruction suited to each category of new personnel and periodic retraining of all employees will be needed to bring about lasting improvement in their work habits and attitudes. In order to reach such a large and diverse audience with the information needed to gain their understanding and participation, a continuing massive educational effort will be required.

Active support by the medical and veterinary professions, as well as the allied groups in such fields as microbiology, public health, home economics, food technology, and animal husbandry, is crucial to the success of the program. There is, however, a tendency to de-emphasize infectious diseases in the formal education of these professional groups and to stress molecular biology even among those specializing in microbiology. Future physicians and scientists are not, therefore, being adequately exposed to the epidemiological concepts that are vitally involved in the control of salmonellosis. The reluctance of practitioners to report or to investigate supposedly isolated cases of diarrhea is a stumbling block to the detection of outbreaks. If this reluctance could be overcome, it would do much to bring about more effective preventive measures.

University curricula in home economics tend to limit emphasis on food preparation to students majoring in dietetics or institutional management, and as a consequence, sanitary aspects of home cookery are not stressed. The large majority of home-economics majors who become high school teachers are, therefore, poorly prepared to instruct their students in the sanitary practices required to prepare food safely.

As the more serious infectious diseases, such as diphtheria and typhoid fever, have become less prevalent, secondary and trade schools, as well as colleges, have tended to equate personal hygiene with making oneself attractive to others, and they have given scant attention to teaching the elements of sanitation that must be practiced at home, on the farm, in the factory, and especially in all food-service operations. An essential aspect of the educational effort is to change this passive attitude among professional and lay groups in order to get their help in persuading others, including patients, housewives, farmers, industry management, employees, and the public at large to accept the inconvenience and costs associated with detection and control of salmonellosis.

Sanitarians and veterinarians constitute the largest professional groups whose work is directed toward the detection and correction of environmental health hazards. They are widely employed by government and industry as consultants, inspectors, and supervisors of sanitation programs relating to water, wastes, milk, meat, shellfish, and other foods. Their contributions to public health practices are often underrated because at times their jobs are given to political appointees who do not have the requisite professional training and experience to do competent work. Implementation of nationwide salmonella control programs will require at least doubling the number of capable sanitarians and veterinary inspectors. They should be encouraged to undertake advanced training to update their technical knowledge and increase their professional status to withstand the pressures that arise when economic interests conflict with good sanitation. Their work is made exceedingly difficult by the conservative attitudes of public prosecutors and the judiciary toward penalizing commercial interests for any but the most flagrant violations of sanitation regulations. Better understanding within the legal profession is needed in order to make full use of existing public health laws in controlling salmonella contamination of commercial products.

Much of the U.S. population has a distorted view of personal hygiene and environmental sanitation, based largely on superficial training at home and in school, as well as on advertising, news releases, and official publications. The public has been led to believe that the protection afforded by government and industry places the safety of any product offered for sale above reproach. While this view is, in large measure, justified for some products, it presents an obstacle to acceptance of the need for additional measures. More stress should, therefore, be given to the fact that major abuses occur during preparation, holding, and serving of food in restaurants and at home. Meals prepared by amateurs for large groups and by institutional food services seem particularly likely to produce outbreaks of salmonellosis and other food-borne diseases that could be prevented by strict observance of sanitation principles. By comparison, the abuses encountered in commercial food-processing operations are relatively infrequent, but they deserve special attention because contamination of such products may subject very large numbers of consumers to the risk of infection.

Comprehensive information on control of diarrheal diseases in institutions is much needed. Buildings occupied by students, religious orders, orphans, elderly persons, criminals, mental patients, and people with physical impairments all present special hazards with respect to dissemination of enteric infections. Hospitals present a unique situation, because the patients are already under stresses that make them more susceptible than the general population. It is essential that institutional administrators be alert to this, so that they may enlist the cooperation of their staff members through "infection control committees" and by personal attention to job performance. Strict sanitary control is necessary to block potential avenues of transmission that involve carriers, food, water, wastes, vermin, aerosols, and general housekeeping. Unfortunately, many existing institutions occupy quarters that were not designed or constructed to facilitate control of disease transmission. Schools of architecture could perform a useful service by teaching the structural requirements for sanitation that are so often overlooked in new or remodeled buildings.

Efforts have been made in recent years by several governmental agencies, educational institutions, and technical and trade associations to inform professional people in and out of industry about the scientific basis for prevention of salmonellosis. At the federal level, the Department of Health, Education, and Welfare and the Department of Agriculture have been active in developing technical information and in collecting data from other sources about the occurrence and control of salmonellosis. Both Departments have sponsored excellent conferences and symposia that were widely attended by technical specialists from government and industry.[3-6] An extensive list of short-term, specialized training courses is offered by several agencies,[7,8] and curricula for training at the college level have been recommended.[9,10] Numerous technical articles and manuals have been published,[11,12] and the National Communicable Disease Center has become nationally recognized as a reference laboratory for identification of unusual serotypes.[13] It has also done much to stimulate epidemiological investigations by other organizations through its Epidemic Intelligence Service and publication of surveillance reports.[14]

Federal agencies have collaborated with state agencies, hospitals, universities, technical and trade associations, and industry groups to obtain, evaluate, and disseminate information among professional workers. However, the available knowledge has yet to be effectively transmitted to the nonprofessional groups whose day-to-day cooperation is necessary. To date, proposals for intensifying these activities have not received budgetary support, but they should be given priority consideration in program planning at the federal level.

Seizures of salmonella-contaminated products by enforcement agencies seem to have done perhaps more to gain the attention of management and their employees than all educational efforts combined. Introduction of new safeguards, such as pasteurization of commercial egg products,[15-17] has also encouraged industry to reassess its processes with respect to elimination of contamination and avoidance of recontamination.

There remains, however, the much more difficult job of crystallizing this interest into a comprehensive national program and sustaining the effort on a long-term basis. To have any reasonable prospect for success, a broadly based education program must be devised that reaches not only professional workers and management but that is also selectively directed to nonprofessional workers and the general public.

While detailed discussion of these problems is beyond the scope of this report, the Committee wishes to call attention to some of the more critical deficiencies and needs. The educational efforts are currently focused on professional people, whereas the greatest need is to provide practical information to individual workers in local governments and industries as well as to homemakers. The dubious assumption is frequently made that individuals who receive training provided by federal agencies and national industry associations will, in turn, pass this information along to other groups whose members will then inform still others. There is, however, relatively little training being done on control of salmonellosis by state and local governments. Presumably, industry groups (e.g., trade associations) can reach their own members, but their publications and training courses, for example, do not reach significant numbers of nonmember operators in the same industry. A number of universities have also made modest contributions by issuing reports[18] and service bulletins on control of salmonellosis,[19] but there is, as yet, no coherent pattern of education on this subject.

Development and implementation of a coordinated federal–state–industry plan for control of salmonellosis appear necessary to generate the technical and financial support required for expanding educational efforts on a continuing basis. Under such a plan, the federal government would be expected to develop the technical basis for a broad educational program and to support the states as well as nongovernmental organizations in carrying the program to the local level. By enlisting the cooperation of subordinate groups, these agencies could, in turn, disseminate the information through a variety of channels, including the secondary and trade schools, universities and colleges, industry training courses, professional conferences, homemakers' and farmers' meetings, and the many publications that are designed to reach special-interest groups. The initial efforts will, in most instances, require reinforcement by retraining to maintain effectiveness.

While much careful planning will be needed to determine the technical points to be emphasized, the more difficult problems relate to (a) devising acceptable effective means for mass education of audiences having diverse backgrounds and interests and (b) generating a desire to use the information on a day-to-day basis. All the electronic and other devices now available as training aids can contribute to the first objective, provided ready sources of accurate interesting material are developed from which the "instructors" can obtain timely information. Slides, movies, television tapes, pamphlets, manuals, instructor's guides, programmed instruction, and other instructional material should be continually revised, and this responsibility alone may demand the full-time effort of one or more highly sophisticated organizations that can present the subject matter in terms suitable, on the one hand, to high school students or skilled workers, and on the other, to highly educated specialists in management, technology, economics, advertising, transportation, and marketing.

In cases where large numbers of workers need training in specific skills and procedures such as are required for sanitary preparation, serving, and holding of food, programmed instruction may be particularly useful, because it allows "self-teaching" of the individual employee on a schedule compatible with his other activities. Development of the instructional materials requires great skill and much effort, but once done, the course can be given with minimal supervision and cost to any number of trainees.

In order to reach the general public, including the housewife, the mass communication media, especially television and women's magazines, seem to offer the greatest promise, if conflicts with advertising interests can be avoided. With some ingenuity, interesting stories can be developed to convey important messages relating to home practices, such as hygienic care of household pets (don't dump the turtle's water in the kitchen sink!) or of new convenience foods (the use and abuse of precooked frozen foods).

Advertisers of food products and equipment have an opportunity to foster improved sanitary practices by illustrating safe procedures of preparing and storing foods. They seem, however, to feel that the use of fingers is more acceptable to the potential buyer than the simplest utensils, and they cannot resist suggesting so-called gourmet dishes that involve lengthy manipulation at temperatures that encourage the growth of microorganisms. A recent newspaper article[20] on salad making says, ". . . begin a thorough mix of all ingredients. (Use your hands and enjoy it.) . . . Watch your guests and ask for comments. . . . If they say things you don't like, ask them to leave; otherwise, have fun."

A conscientious effort on the part of food editors and advertising sponsors to avoid questionable practices could have a far-reaching effect on the attitudes of their audiences toward food sanitation. Hopefully, recommendations of improved practices might, in some instances, serve their commercial interests as well as the public.

Practical solutions to the problems of motivation are not obvious, and continuing reappraisal of efforts in this direction will be needed. There appears to be no valid precedent to guide the salmonella control program, though the management policies of industry and government can be very influential. One aspect that deserves consideration is the possibility of presenting the subject to the public on a basis of environmental sanitation in which salmonellosis is the focal point or model. However, the appeal would be to safety, cleanliness, aesthetic sensibilities, and giving the consumer more for his money.

Leadership at the national level is vital to develop a consensus among governmental agencies, industry associations, labor unions, public information media, and school systems regarding the main thrust and timing of educational programs that will complement other actions intended to minimize the spread of salmonellosis by environmental vehicles. Identification and evaluation of specific goals, available resources, instructional techniques, key audiences, and priority problems are prerequisites to launching an intensive national program. Its success may well depend on convincing the public that the cost-to-benefit ratio is in its favor and on making diarrheal disease, including salmonellosis, a household word that offends the sensibilities whenever it is associated with man's environment. In any event, the effective control of salmonellosis in the United States depends heavily on developing a continuing nationwide educational and training program that will inform, motivate, and periodically retrain the multitude of individuals who must help to improve the level of environmental sanitation. Such a program can be effective only when its teachings are put into practice.

REFERENCES

1. National Restaurant Association, *Facts About the Food Service Industry*, Nat. Rest. Ass., 1530 N. Lake Shore Drive, Chicago, Ill. (1968).
2. H. A. Montague, "Food Service Manpower Requirements for an Expanding Industry," Appendix A, pp. 39–42, in *Report of the Conference on Food Service Industry Manpower and Education*, Nat. Rest. Ass., Chicago, Ill. (1967).
3. *Salmonellosis—Proc. Nat. Conf. Salmonellosis*, Pub. Health Serv. Publ. No. 1262, Nat. Communicable Disease Center, Atlanta, Georgia (1965).

4. U.S. Department of Health, Education, and Welfare, *Proceedings of the Interdepartmental Conference on Salmonellosis,* June 3-4, 1965, Food and Drug Administration, Washington, D.C.
5. U.S. Department of Agriculture, *The Destruction of Salmonellae; A Report of the Western Experiment Station Collaborators' Conference, Albany, California, March 9-11, 1966,* Agr. Res. Ser. Publ. 74-37, Washington, D.C. (July 1966).
6. U.S. Department of Agriculture, *Proceedings of the Salmonella Seminar Held at Federal Center Building Hyattsville, Maryland, May 4-5, 1964,* Agr. Res. Ser. Publ. 91-50, Hyattsville, Md. (Dec. 1964).
7. U.S. Department of Health, Education, and Welfare, *National Communicable Disease Center Training Bulletin, January 1, 1968 to June 30, 1969,* NCDC, Atlanta, Ga.
8. U.S. Department of Health, Education, and Welfare, *National Center for Urban and Industrial Health Bulletin of Courses, July 1968 to June 1969,* Cincinnati, Ohio.
9. U.S. Department of Health, Education, and Welfare, Office of Education, *Food Processing Technology—A Suggested Two-Year Post High School Curriculum,* U.S. Gov. Printing Office, Washington, D.C. (1967).
10. U.S. Department of Health, Education, and Welfare, Office of Education, *Quantity Food Preparation, a Suggested Guide,* U.S. Gov. Printing Office, Washington, D.C. (1967).
11. R. P. Elliott, ed., *Bacteriological Analytical Manual,* U.S. Dep. of Health, Education, and Welfare, Food and Drug Administration, Washington, D.C. (1966).
12. K. H. Lewis and R. Angelotti, eds., *Examination of Foods for Enteropathogenic and Indicator Bacteria,* Pub. Health Ser. Publ. No. 1142, U.S. Gov. Printing Office, Washington, D.C. (1964).
13. W. J. Martin, M. M. Ball, A. C. McWhorter, and S. F. Bartes, *Quarterly Summary of Salmonella Cultures Received from the United States and Its Territories,* NCDC, Atlanta, Ga. (from October 1966 to present).
14. U.S. Department of Health, Education, and Welfare, *Salmonella Surveillance,* NCDC, Atlanta, Ga. (issued monthly, 1963 to present).
15. U.S. Department of Agriculture, *Egg Pasteurization Manual,* Unpublished Review Copy, Agr. Res. Ser., West. Util. Res. and Dev. Div., Albany, Calif. (1967).
16. U.S. Department of Health, Education, and Welfare, *Ordinance and Code Regulating the Processing of Eggs and Egg Products—1968 Recommendations of the Public Health Service* (Undergoing clearance for publication).
17. U.S. Department of Health, Education, and Welfare, Food and Drug Administration, *Eggs and Egg Products, Part 42, Federal Register, 4677* (1966).
18. F. J. McArdle (conference chairman), p. 220, in *Proceedings—Salmonellae in Foods Conference,* College of Agriculture, Univ. of Pa., University Park, Pa. (March 1968).
19. E. A. Zottola, *Salmonellosis,* Extension Bulletin 339, Agr. Ext. Ser., Univ. of Minnesota (April 1967).
20. K. McCabe, *It's a Hustle-Bustle Life, but There's Time for All,* p. 3, in *The Cincinnati Enquirer,* Food Section, (Wednesday, Aug. 14, 1968).

14 Research

Although salmonellosis has been known for more than half a century, the gaps in our knowledge of its epidemiology are still considerable. As yet there is no effective agent available for chemoprophylaxis and therapy of salmonella food poisoning and enteritis. The factors of host susceptibility are poorly understood, and there is no effective vaccine. Nor is there adequate understanding by laymen, physicians, and others of effective control of this common malady. It is for these reasons that, throughout this report, areas in need of further research have been identified. Research, together with more effective application of feasible control measures, should significantly contribute to improved public health.

APPENDIXES

Appendix A

The Most Commonly Occurring
Salmonella Serotypes
(The Genus *Salmonella*)

An abbreviated Antigenic Schema consisting of the commonly occurring salmonellae is listed in Table A1. Antigenic formulas are included for the information of readers who may not be familiar with serotypic classification of *Salmonella* by antigen analysis. Further, data on the occurence of these serotypes among cultures submitted to the National Salmonella Center during the period 1948–1958 and information from another source (i.e., the Salmonella Surveillance Summary) for the year 1967 are presented in Table A1 for comparison.

Data regarding the occurrence and sources of the 25 most frequently occurring serotypes (and variants of serotypes) among cultures submitted to the National Salmonella Center between October 1, 1966, and September 30, 1967, are given in Table A2. The data on frequency given in Table A2 may be compared with those in Table A3, which lists the 25 most common serotypes of *Salmonella* (ranked from 1 to 25) as reported in the Salmonella Summaries for the years 1963 through 1967.

References to the sources of the information given in Tables A1–A3 can be found in Chapter 5.

TABLE A1 Antigenic Formulas and Ranks of Commonly Occurring Salmonellae[a]

| Species and Serotype | Group | Antigenic Formula | | | (a) 23,414 | | (b) 19,723 | |
		O Antigens	H antigens Phase 1	Phase 2	No.	Rank[b]	No.	Rank[b]
S. enteritidis, bioser. Paratyphi A	A	1, 2, 12	a	—	33	*37*	7	*44*
ser. Paratyphi B	B	1, 4, 5, 12	b	1, 2	267	*8*	173	*20*
ser. Paratyphi B, Odense	**B**	1, 4, 12	b	1, 2	4	*47*	—	*—*
bioser. Java	B	1, 4, 5, 12	b	(1, 2)	211	*11*	309	*14*
ser. Stanley	B	4, 5, 12	d	1, 2	20	*41*	7	*44*
ser. Schwarzengrund	B	1, 4, 12, 27	d	1, 7	52	*30*	72	*26*
ser. Saint paul	B	1, 4, 5, 12	e, h	1, 2	108	*22*	907	*6*
ser. Reading	B	4, 5, 12	e, h	1, 5	216	*10*	54	*32*
ser. Chester	B	4, 5, 12	e, h	e, n, x	87	*24*	100	*23*
ser. San diego	B	4, 12	e, h	e, n, z_{15}	182	*15*	149	*21*
ser. Derby	B	1, 4, 5, 12	f, g	—	157	*19*	326	*13*
ser. California	B	4, 5, 12	m, t	—	60	*27*	16	*40*
ser. Typhimurium	B	1, 4, 5, 12	i	1, 2	1479	*1*	5530	*1*
ser. Typhimurium, Copenhagen	B	1, 4, 12	i	1, 2	70	*26*	273	*17*
ser. Bredeney	B	1, 4, 12	l, v	1, 7	91	*23*	120	*22*
ser. Heidelberg	B	1, 4, 5, 12	r	1, 2	176	*16*	1648	*2*
S. cholerae-suis	C_1	6, 7	c	1, 5	16	*43*	6	*45*
S. cholerae-suis, bioser. Kunzendorf	C_1	6, 7	(c)	1, 5	236	*9*	20	*38*
S. enteritidis, ser. Braenderup	C_1	6, 7	eh	e, n, z_{15}	26	*38*	83	*24*
ser. Montevideo	C_1	6, 7	g, m, s	—	554	*4*	398	*11*
ser. Oranienburg	C_1	6, 7	m, t	—	632	*3*	406	*10*

Serotype	Group	O antigen	H phase 1	H phase 2				
ser. Thompson	C_1	6,7	k	1,5	153	20	508	*9*
ser. Infantis	C_1	6,7	r	1,5	188	14	980	*5*
ser. Bareilly	C_1	6,7	y	1,5	191	13	81	*25*
ser. Tennessee	C_1	6,7	z_{29}	—	296	7	63	*29*
ser. Muenchen	C_2	6,8	d	1,2	347	5	217	*18*
ser. Manhattan	C_2	6,8	d	1,5	86	25	284	*16*
ser. Newport	C_2	6,8	e,h	1,2	739	2	1263	*4*
ser. Blockley	C_2	6,8	k	1,5	56	28	519	*8*
ser. Litchfield	C_2	6,8	l,v	1,2	24	40	81	*25*
ser. Tallahassee	C_2	6,8	z_4, z_{23}	—	12	44	6	*45*
ser. Kentucky	C_2	(8),20	i	z_6	46	31	40	*34*
bioser. Miami	D	1,9,12	a	1,5	39	34	69	*27*
S. typhi		9,12,Vi	d	—	°	°	690°	*7°*
S. enteritidis, ser. Enteritidis	D	1,9,12	g,m	—	174	17	1277	*3*
ser. Berta	D	9,12	f,g,t	—	25	39	37	*35*
ser. Dublin	D	1,9,12	g,p	—	5	46	8	*43*
ser. Panama	D	1,9,12	l,v	1,5	169	18	182	*19*
ser. Javiana	D	1,9,12	l,z_{28}	1,5	196	12	373	*12*
bioser. Pullorum	D	9,12	—	—	38	35	3	*47*
ser. Anatum	E_1	3,10	e,h	1,6	320	6	297	*15*
ser. Meleagridis	E_1	3,10	e,h	1,w	45	32	7	*44*
ser. Give	E_1	3,10	l,v	1,7	119	21	61	*30*
ser. Newington	E_2	3,15	e,h	1,6	41	33	43	*33*
ser. Illinois	E_3	(3),(15),34	z_{10}	1,5	2	48	1	*49*
ser. Senftenberg	E_4	1,13,19	g,s,t	—	52	30	58	*31*
ser. Simsbury	E_4	1,13,19	z_{27}	—	4	47	4	*46*
ser. Rubislaw	F	11	r	e,n,x	26	38	24	*36*

TABLE A1—continued

Species and Serotype	Antigenic Formula				(a) 23,414		(b) 19,723	
	Group	O Antigens	H antigens Phase 1	Phase 2	No.	Rank[b]	No.	Rank[b]
ser. Poona	G	13, 22	z	1, 6	33	37	58	31
ser. Worthington	G	1, 13, 23	z	1, w	53	29	24	36
ser. Cubana	G	1, 13, 23	z_{29}	—	52	30	66	28
ser. Florida	H	1, 6, 14, 25	d	1, 7	6	45	2	48
ser. Madelia	H	1, 6, 14, 25	y	1, 7	16	43	8	43
ser. Cerro	18	18	z_4, z_{23}	—	12	44	9	42
ser. Siegburg	18	6, 14, 18	z_4, z_{23}	—	36	36	10	41
ser. Minnesota	21	21	b	e, n, x	26	38	22	37
ser. Urbana	30	30	b	e, n, x	19	42	18	39

[a] Rank of *Salmonella* from human sources that occurred most frequently among 23,414 cultures (a) received in the period July 1, 1948 through June 30, 1958 compared with 19,723 (b) reported for 1967 in the Annual Summary of Salmonella Surveillance.

[b] Italic figures in the "Rank" column indicate the 25 species and serotypes that occurred most frequently among cultures from human sources.

[c] The figures for *S. typhi* are weighted because of repeated examinations of cultures from both cases and carriers.

182

TABLE A2 Most Commonly Occurring Serotypes of *Salmonella* Received in the Enteric Bacteriology Unit, NCDC, October 1, 1966–September 30, 1967

Species and Serotype	Group	Human									Other Sources						Human Total[a]	Other Sources and Human Totals[a]
		0–6 mo.	6 mo.–1 yr.	1–5 yr.	5–20 yr.	>20 yr.	Un-known	Case	Convalescent Carrier	Contact Carrier	Un-known	Ani-mal	Food	H_2O	Unk.	Misc.		
Salmonella enteritidis																		
ser. Anatum	E_1	3	2	—	1	9	4	12	—	3	—	11	16	10			19(13)	56(8)
ser. Binza	E_2	2	1	—	—	—	—	1	—	1	—	—	12	5			3(24)	20(19)
ser. Blockley	C_2	1	1	4	3	9	9	24	—	—	—	1	1	12			27(11)	41(13)
ser. Bredeney	B	2	—	—	—	1	1	2	—	—	—	3	—	10			4(23)	17(21)
ser. Chester	B	—	—	1	—	2	6	6	—	1	—	4	—	—			9(19)	13(23)
ser. Cubana	G	1	—	3	—	1	3	6	—	2	—	1	2	11			8(20)	22(17)
ser. Derby	B	3	1	7	—	7	3	12	—	4	—	11	5	11			21(12)	48(11)
ser. Enteritidis	D	3	1	7	6	25	20	40	—	1	—	—	1	4			62(5)	67(6)
ser. Give	E_1	2	1	1	—	2	—	5	—	—	—	1	—	11			6(22)	18(20)
ser. Heidelberg	B	4	3	11	9	12	12	37	1	2	—	—	—	50			51(6)	101(5)
ser. Infantis	C_1	5	4	9	3	9	11	28	1	—	—	1	1	13			41(9)	56(8)
Bioser. Java	B	2	1	9	2	13	17	33	—	—	—	1	3	6			44(7)	54(9)
ser. Javiana	D	9	2	13	7	7	4	37	—	—	—	5	1	1			42(8)	49(10)
ser. Manhattan	C_2	2	4	3	2	4	3	11	—	3	—	4	—	5			18(14)	27(15)
ser. Meleagridis	E_1	1	—	—	—	1	—	2	—	—	—	—	—	—			2(25)	2
ser. Montevideo	C_1	1	—	—	2	4	9	11	—	—	—	1	1	21			16(16)	39(14)
ser. Muenchen	C_3	1	—	—	5	6	—	11	—	—	—	—	2	6			12(18)	20(19)
ser. Newport	C_3	5	7	21	24	27	13	81	—	6	—	7	1	15			97(4)	120(4)
ser. Oranienburg	C_1	—	2	—	5	4	6	10	1	—	—	1	1	26			17(15)	45(12)
ser. Panama	D	—	—	1	7	2	8	9	—	—	—	2	—	5			18(14)	25(16)
ser. Paratyphi B	B	—	1	4	3	4	2	7	1	—	—	—	—	—			14(17)	14(22)
ser. Saint paul	B	3	—	8	4	8	17	29	—	3	—	—	1	13			40(10)	54(9)

183

TABLE A2—continued

Species and Serotype	Group	Human									Other Sources						Human Total[a]	Other Sources and Human Totals[a]
		0-6 mo.	6 mo.-1 yr.	1-5 yr.	5-20 yr.	>20 yr.	Un-known	Case	Convalescent Carrier	Contact Carrier	Un-known	Animal	Food	H_2O	Unk.	Misc.		
ser. San diego	B	1	1	3	—	6	1	9	—	—	3	4	3	2	—	—	12(18)	21(18)
ser. Schwarzengrund	B	—	—	—	—	—	—	—	—	—	—	—	1	9	—	—	—	10(24)
ser. Senftenberg	E_4	—	—	2	—	—	—	2	—	—	—	3	2	—	—	—	2(25)	7(25)
ser. Tennessee	C_1	1	—	2	4	1	—	3	1	1	3	1	1	7	1	—	8(20)	18(20)
ser. Thompson	C_1	5	2	17	29	62	47	86	—	9	67	4	22	21	—	2	162(3)	211(3)
S. typhi[b]	D	1	—	12	39	97	74	66	3	47	107	—	—	—	—	—	223(2)	223(2)
S. enteritidis																		
ser. Typhimurium	B	25	21	68	61	107	134	309	1	14	92	7	35	69	—	1	416(1)	528(1)
ser. Typhimurium var. cop.	B	7	4	9	2	11	18	36	—	3	12	1	—	14	—	—	51(6)	66(7)
ser. Worthington	G	—	1	—	1	—	1	1	—	—	2	1	—	2	—	—	3(24)	6
ser. Bareilly	C_1	1	—	2	—	1	—	2	—	1	1	—	—	—	—	—	4(23)	4
ser. Litchfield	C_2	—	—	2	1	1	3	4	—	—	3	—	—	—	—	—	7(21)	—
TOTALS		90	59	216	215	429	450	932	8	103	416	75	113	358	1	3	1459	2009
Percent (calc. from below)[c]		4.5	2.9	10.8	10.7	21.4	22.4	46.4	0.4	5.1	20.7	3.7	5.6	17.8	—	—	72.6	—
Percent (calc. as indicated from totals)[e]		6.2	4.0	14.8	14.7	29.4	30.8	63.9	0.5	7.1	28.5[d]	13.6	20.5	65.1	—	—[f]	58.4	80.4

[a] Number in parentheses indicates rank with regard to frequency of occurrence.

[b] The figures for S. typhi are weighted because of repeat examinations of cultures from both cases and carriers.

[c] 1459 Human total.

[d] 550 Other sources total.

[e] 2009 over-all total of these serotypes.

[f] 2498 yearly total of all Salmonella serotypes.

TABLE A3 The Twenty-Five Most Commonly Occuring Species and Serotypes of *Salmonella* in Man (Ranked 1 to 25) Compared with Numbers Isolated from Other Sources (from Annual Summaries, NCDC Salmonella Surveillance)

Species and Serotype	Group	1963 Human[a]	1963 Other Sources	1964 Human[a]	1964 Other Sources	1965 Human[a]	1965 Other Sources	1966 Human[a]	1966 Other Sources	1967 Human[a]	1967 Other Sources
S. enteritidis											
ser. Anatum	E₁	224(14)	270	279(14)	20	300(14)	269	333(14)	441	297(15)	521
ser. Bareilly	C₁	59	23	99	26	104	33	78	30	81(25)	51
ser. Blockley	C₂	360(11)	125	427(11)	114	401(12)	213	603(8)	194	519(8)	115
ser. Braenderup	C₁	56	6	102	20	85	25	111(25)	38	83(24)	84
ser. Bredeney	B	153(22)	116	220(18)	109	160(21)	110	159(19)	86	120(22)	174
ser. Bredeney	B	190(16)	96	75	181	115	184	109	153	100(23)	52
ser. Chester	G	40	28	63	32	145(22)	25	131(23)	219	66	243
ser. Cubana	B	1610(2)	114	2360(2)	213	632(8)	106	404(10)	266	326(13)	458
ser. Derby	D	801(6)	70	801(6)	89	1065(5)	53	1237(5)	87	1277(3)	128
ser. Enteritidis	E₁	65	48	79	38	116(25)	95	78	55	61	55
ser. Give	B	1533(3)	365	1717(3)	483	1621(2)	831	1622(2)	786	1648(2)	665
ser. Heidelberg	C₁	970(5)	347	1523(4)	362	1145(4)	385	1315(4)	368	980(5)	424
ser. Infantis	D	168(19)	5	256(16)	1	361(13)	11	312(15)	8	373(12)	32
ser. Javiana	C₂	67	22	69	16	96	18	97	19	81(25)	4
ser. Litchfield	C₂	192(15)	32	181(21)	47	125(24)	47	134(21)	42	284(16)	38
ser. Manhattan	E₁	82	18	48	47	140(23)	80	8	25	7	53
ser. Meleagridis	C₁	490(10)	253	524(10)	215	458(11)	213	337(13)	346	398(11)	335
ser. Montevideo	C₂	265(13)	74	261(15)	86	219(16)	50	229(17)	69	217(18)	96
ser. Muenchen	C₂	1080(4)	203	1036(5)	161	1257(3)	203	1319(3)	159	1263(4)	154
ser. Newport	C₁	539(9)	99	550(9)	149	591(9)	190	399(11)	183	406(10)	260
ser. Oranienburg											

TABLE A3—continued

Species and Serotype	Group	1963 Human[a]	1963 Other Sources	1964 Human[a]	1964 Other Sources	1965 Human[a]	1965 Other Sources	1966 Human[a]	1966 Other Sources	1967 Human[a]	1967 Other Sources
ser. Panama	D	141(24)	12	189(20)	27	229(15)	32	274(16)	23	182(19)	62
ser. Paratyphi B	B	175(17)	4	175(23)	1	177(19)	7	153(20)	9	173(20)	—
bioser. Java	B	155(21)	3	231(17)	5	199(18)	25	367(12)	51	309(14)	—
ser. Saint paul	B	586(8)	206	645(8)	194	767(6)	273	737(6)	334	907(6)	381
ser. San diego	B	120(25)	69	178(22)	85	229(15)	158	122(24)	110	149(21)	91
ser. Schwarzengrund	B	147(23)	191	155(24)	106	114	162	71	276	72	152
ser. Senftenberg	E4	33	39	108(25)	86	74	127	72	188	58	274
ser. Tennessee	C1	164(20)	88	332(13)	119	173(20)	117	133(22)	206	63	322
ser. Thompson	C1	321(12)	90	421(12)	133	562(10)	198	579(9)	203	508(9)	209
S. typhi[b]	D	706(7)	2	703(7)	—	719(7)	—	654(7)	—	690(7)	—
S. enteritidis											
ser. Typhimurium	B	5435(1)	1065	5656(1)	942	6526(1)	978	5744(1)	884	5530(1)	896
ser. Typhimurium var. cop.	B	173(18)	260	206(19)	153	203(17)	282	178(18)	203	273(17)	250
SUBTOTAL (ranks 1 to 25)		16,698	4,343	19,134	4,490	18,520	5,501	17,586	6,062	17,174	6,579
		89.5[c]	80.6	91.0	82.2	88.8	80.5	87.8	78.6	87.1	74.8
TOTAL all serotypes (100%)		18,649	5,389	21,113	5,461	20,865	6,834	20,040	7,709	19,723	8,794

[a] Number in parentheses indicates rank with regard to frequency of occurrence in humans (ranks 1 to 25).
[b] The figures for S. typhi are weighted because of repeat examinations of cultures from both cases and carriers.
[c] Percent of total, all serotypes.

Appendix B

Apparent Genetic Plasticity of *Salmonella*, Resistance Factors, and Use of Antibiotics in Feeds

There has been much speculation on the significance of the apparent genetic plasticity of salmonellae in relation to disease in man and other animals. But as far as is now known, genetic changes in cultures of *Salmonella* have little or no effect upon their ability to cause infection or to produce symptoms of disease. Variations in the antigenic structure of strains of *Salmonella* do not detract one iota from the value of serologic analysis and the use of the antigenic schema in epidemiologic investigations. Similarly, the very occasional occurrence of biochemical variants does not interfere with characterization of salmonellae by biochemical methods.

The genetic plasticity of salmonellae is more apparent than real, since salmonellae probably are no more or less plastic than other members of the family Enterobacteriaceae (e.g., *Escherichia coli, Shigella, Serratia, Proteus*), or members of other families of bacteria, fungi, and protozoa.[1-6]

Similarly, the large number of known serotypes of *Salmonella* is not of great significance to salmonellosis *per se,* since it is well known that a relatively small number of serotypes are involved in a very high percentage of infections in both man and animals throughout the world (Chapter 5 and Appendix A).

Much of the progress made in bacterial genetics during the past 20 years has involved the use of members of the various genera of Enterobacteriaceae. Since considerable information already was available that dealt with the *natural* variational phenomena, of the O (somatic) and H (flagellar) antigens of salmonellae, and since an antigenic schema in which the serotypes could be oriented was available, the potentialities of salmonellae in genetic investigations were quickly recognized. Studies made in 1952 and 1953[7, 8] dealt with transduction and marked the beginning of an era of investigation of the genetics of salmonellae. Since then serotypes of *Salmonella* have been employed in investigations of the genetics of O, H, and R (rough) variations, as well as resistance to antimicrobial agents, and hundreds of publications have resulted. The fact that salmonellae have been studied so intensely by so many investigators may have given rise to the concept of apparent genetic plasticity.

NATURAL VARIATIONS

It should be emphasized that there are several kinds of variation that occur in members of the genus *Salmonella,* in nature and in the laboratory, and that do not require the presence of a bacteriophage. Some of these natural variations have been known since 1903,[9, 10] and all are of importance in antigenic analysis of *Salmonella.* In fact their discovery and elucidation was essential to the development of the antigenic schema. These natural variations are:

1. Loss of H (flagellar) antigens, HO to O (nonmotile)
2. Reversible phase variation of Andrewes in H antigens, e.g., $\underline{i} \longleftrightarrow \underline{1,2}$
3. Loss of variation in H antigens: loss of phase 1 or of phase 2 antigens, giving rise to monophasic forms
4. Form variation in certain O antigens: quantitative variation in the amount of certain antigens present in the progeny of a strain
5. S (smooth) to R (rough), and S to T (transitional) to R variations
6. KO to O variations such as ViO to O(V-W) and MO to O

These and other kinds of natural variation are, of course, controlled genetically or involve the genetic constitution of the bacteria in some manner. However, with the exception of phase variation of Andrewes, which is known only in members of the genera *Salmonella* and *Arizona,* all these variations occur in other Enterobacteriaceae and in many other families of bacteria as well.[11]

VARIATIONS MEDIATED BY BACTERIOPHAGE OR OTHER MECHANISMS

There are at least three kinds of genetic mechanisms that affect salmonellae, but not salmonellae alone.[12] These are transduction, lysogenic (or phage) conversion, and conjugation.

1. Zinder and Lederberg[7] proved that a temperate phage called PLT 22, affecting members of O antigen groups A, B, and D, could introduce genetic material into susceptible cells and hence effect transfer (transduction) of H antigens or of physiological characters from donor to recipient cells. Lederberg and Edwards[8] produced a number of recombinants using PLT 22, and Kauffmann[13] effected similar changes in members of O groups A and B with other (different) temperate phages. Edwards *et al.*[14] characterized temperate phages that were capable of transducing H antigens in members of O antigen groups of *Salmonella* other than those mentioned above. Several investigators[15-18] were able to accomplish transductions with virulent phages by means of specialized techniques.

2. In lysogenic conversion[19] the phage genes as such are thought to function as part of the bacterial cells. The state of lysogenicity *per se,* caused by infection with a phage that has converting properties or capabilities, brings about changes in the O antigens. As long as the organism remains lysogenic (i.e., as long as the phage is present) these changes persist, and the particular O antigen can be demonstrated. Conversely, when the state of lysogenicity is lost (i.e., when the converting phage is lost) the O antigen involved then cannot be detected. It long has been known that O antigen 1, for example, is present in certain bacteria within O group A and absent in variant forms of the same bacteria. O antigen 1 also may occur in serotypes in other O groups or may be absent in variant forms of the same serotypes. This kind of variation now is known to be dependent upon whether the particular culture has been lysogenized. However, this should not be confused with *form* variation. In transduction experiments in which H antigens were transduced to strains of O group A, Kauffmann[13] noted that O antigen 1 also was transferred. The majority of the O antigens of *Salmonella* that are known to be subject to lysogenic conversion are recorded in Table 12 of the

review by Lüderitz et al.[20] together with references. (The phages listed as Xi in Table 12 of that review should be labeled epsilon, however.) The O antigens listed there are 1, 6, 12₂, 14, 15, 20, 27, 34, 37, and 42₂, and the somatic groups involved are A, B, C₁, C₂, D, E, G, K, R, and T. Since the above-mentioned review was written, additional papers have appeared that deal with lysogenic conversion. For example, LeMinor[21] reported that cultures of O group 51 that possessed O antigen 1 were lysogenic, and that the phage released by these cultures lysogenized strains of 051 which then acquired factor 1. However, the 1 factor of 1, 51 strains was not identical with that of other O groups in which factor 1 occurred. Extensive investigations of members of groups C₁ and C₂ also have been described.[22, 23]

3. Recombination of characteristics also occurs by means of conjugation of E. coli and Salmonella as shown by Baron et al.[24] and Zinder[25] and by conjugation between different salmonellae.[26] Hybrids produced by conjugation usually have been selected and recognized by means of biochemical characters. However, transfer of antigenic characters through sexual processes, i.e., the transfer of the H antigens of both phase 1 and phase 2 of S. enteritidis serotype Abony (4, 5, 12:b:e, n, x) to E. coli has been demonstrated.[27] Also changes in the O antigens have been effected by conjugation,[28-30] and conjugation has been utilized in studies on S, R, S-R, and T antigens of salmonellae.[31, 32]

Sexduction, or F-duction,[6, 12] may differ from conjugation only in the amount of the chromosomal segment transferred. Certain genetic elements that may be transferred during conjugation have been shown to be independent of chromosomal transfer. These elements (episomes) alternate between a state of fixed attachment to the chromosome and autonomy.

Transmission of colicinogeny between certain strains of serotype Typhimurium also has been demonstrated[33]—the ability to produce certain colicines was transferred to serotype Typhimurium (strain LT 2) when grown in broth with colicinogenic cultures of E. coli and Shigella sonnei. Some colicine factors were readily transmissible, some were transmitted at a very low rate, and some gave no evidence of transfer. All 20 of the "wild" serotype Typhimurium cultures made colicinogenic and shown to produce colicine I readily transferred colicinogeny to serotype Typhimurium strain LT 2 cys D- 36 str-r, but none of the 12 "wild" strains that were found to produce colicine E2 appears to transmit colicinogeny.[33] "Only a fraction (10^{-3} to 10^{-4}) of the bacteria in a broth culture of an LT 2 strain carrying col I actually transmits the factor and it appears that during long incubation of a mixed culture, col I spreads 'epidemically' in the acceptor population."[33]

It is evident that the effects of genetic recombination cannot be ignored, especially in serotyping. The roles of the phenomena of recombination in the origin of serotypes of *Salmonella* have been the subject of much speculation, and no one now denies that the various kinds of recombination might give rise to new serotypes in nature. Of the mechanisms mentioned, lysogenic conversion probably has the most influence on serotypic identity and epidemiology, since each lysogenized organism undergoes antigenic change. In a classic example, both *S. enteritidis* serotype Anatum and *S. enteritidis* serotype Newington were present in the outbreak of disease from which both types were first isolated.[34, 35] The two serotypes have often been found in association, and now it is apparent that the factor determining their identity is infection of serotype Newington by phage epsilon 15. Likewise, the presence or absence of O antigens 1 and 27 in certain serotypes is not necessarily of epidemiologic significance. The list of antigens in this category is increasing, and other instances involving lysogenic conversion are known.[20-22] A few examples follow:

Group C_1 ($\underline{6}, \underline{7}$)	Group C_4 ($\underline{6}, \underline{7}, \underline{14}$)	H antigens
serotype Lille	serotype Bornum	z_{38}
serotype Livingstone	serotype Eimsbuettel	$\underline{d}:\underline{1}, \underline{w}$
serotype Ohio	serotype Nienstedten	$\underline{b}:\underline{1}, \underline{w}$
serotype Oranienburg	serotype Thielallee	$\underline{m}, \underline{t}$
serotype Amersfoort	serotype Omderman	$\underline{d}:\underline{e}, \underline{n}, \underline{x}$

The extent to which transduction and conjugation enter into serotypic changes that have epidemiologic implications is debatable. Within recent years, unusually complex serologic types have been encountered that appear to have arisen by recombination. The first of these, *S. enteritidis* serotype Salinatis ($\underline{4}, \underline{12}:\underline{d}, \underline{e}, \underline{h}:\underline{d}, \underline{e}, \underline{n}, z_{15}$), which possessed the major H antigen d in both phases, was reported by Edwards and Bruner.[36] More recently, a number of similar types have been found.[37-40] These complex serotypes may spontaneously lose a major antigen and then be indistinguishable from well-known "normal" types of *Salmonella*. The most frequently encountered example is serotype Senftenberg ($\underline{1}, \underline{3}, \underline{19}:\underline{g}, \underline{s}, \underline{t}$), which has been found repeatedly with one or another of several different H antigens ($z_{27}, z_{37}, z_{43}, z_{45}$, or z_{46}). While these antigens completely mask agglutination in g, s, t serum,[41] they may be lost spontaneously, and the cultures then behave as typical strains of serotype Senftenberg.

Occasionally, cultures possessing three or even four reversible H phases have been found in nature[42]; they also have been observed to occur during experiments in transduction[43] and in conjugation.[44] Triphasic or quadriphasic cultures may spontaneously lose the ability to produce one or two phases and return to a stable diphasic state. Although such strains are rarely found they may cause confusion in serotyping, and unless the possibility of such occurrences is recognized, possible epidemiologic connections between certain strains may not be recognized. The phenomena mentioned above may be related to the duplication of phases discussed by Lederberg.[45]

The above-mentioned effects of genetic change on *Salmonella* do not diminish in any way the value of serological analysis to epidemiology. Exceptional cultures such as those mentioned occur rarely, and the salmonellae seen in daily practice are ordinarily perfectly typical in their serological characteristics. Even such organisms as serotypes Anatum and Newington, which are lysogenic counterparts, occur separately much more frequently than in association.

Similarly, biochemically atypical cultures of *Salmonella* are rare.[46, 47] They receive undue attention, perhaps, because papers are written about them rather than about the thousands of typical strains. Even when an atypical strain becomes epidemic in a hospital or urban community, it still is only a single strain giving rise to multiple isolations. Furthermore, a strain of serotype Newington that ferments lactose, for example, produces symptoms in the same manner as one that does not.[48] Similarly, a culture of *S. typhi,* into which ability to ferment lactose had been induced, produced typical typhoid fever.[49]

Thus it is apparent that it is the *rate* at which the changes are effected by various genetic mechanisms that is important to the question of apparent genetic plasticity in *Salmonella*. Many factors affect the rate.

In transduction, and apparently in the majority of the other known mechanisms, high titered phages are required[7, 8]; the phage must be relatively nonlethal; both a donor and a susceptible recipient or acceptor must be present, genetic materials must be homologous, and the environment must be favorable. How often are these all present under near optimum conditions in nature? Perhaps once in millions or billions of instances, since even under optimum conditions the maximum frequency of transduction of any one character in serotype Typhimurium was 2×10^{-6}.[7] According to Zinder and Lederberg,[7] "Both sexual recombination and transduction, because of their low frequency, allow only limited gene interchange in bacteria. Transductive exchange is limited both in frequency and extent." The frequency of successful transduction was so low (about one per million phages per trait) as to preclude coincidental transduction of two unrelated factors in any feasible experiment.[7] Transduction apparently is unidirectional, each phage particle producing only one transduced clone (no more than one trait to a single bacterium), although some instances of linked transduction are known, according to Ravin.[6]

In the work of Lederberg and Edwards,[8] the need for high titered phages was again demonstrated, and Edwards et al.[14] reported that in no instance was antigenic transfer (transduction) accomplished with lysates that produced fewer than 5×10^9 plaques per ml. These investigators[14] demonstrated homology of genetic material in donor and recipient.

Bailey[50] demonstrated that of 115 cultures of serotype Typhimurium isolated from various sources, 14 (12.1 percent) carried transducing phage. However, these phages initially were of low titer and had to be propagated and selected (to high titer) in order to effect transduction. Others[8-14] have reported comparable results. Similarly, high titer phages are required for lysogenic conversion,[22] but they apparently need not be as high as those needed for transduction. There is considerable variation in the ease with which strains can be converted.

In conjugation, genetic material flows from one conjugant to the other, but in only one direction. Progeny bearing recombined characters of the two parents are found in only one of two clones. The donor bacterium possesses an agent called the fertility factor (F+), which effects changes in the protein constituents of the cell membrane of the donor. The protein differences in the membranes of donor and recipient bacteria are believed to account for the coupling phenonemon that precedes transfer of genetic material. Most donors transmit nothing more than F+ factors to the conjugating F− recipient, but rare mutant donors transmit large groups of genes and at the same time transmit F+ factors at a greatly reduced rate. These mutant donors are called Hfr because, when isolated, they can transfer genetic material at high frequency. In the usual F+ population, the frequency of recombinants bearing a given donor gene is of the order of 10^{-5}, whereas the frequency of such recombinants obtained when an Hfr donor is used may be as high as 10^{-1} couplings.[7-12] Fertility factors sometimes carry genes (or genetic material), and when they do they are capable of transferring by infection the specific genetic material that they carry, a process called sexduction. Fertility factors and phages form a class of genetic agents called episomes. Episomes that are receiving considerable attention at this time are the R (resistance) factors.

Genetic studies with salmonellae and other bacteria have taught us a great deal about *why* certain variations occur. Also, transduction has been put to practical use in the production of mutants that are useful in absorbing antisera[14] and in determining the H antigens of certain nonmotile strains.[51] Finally, it should be said that if the known genetic mechanisms that affect the antigenic and biochemical reactions of *Sal-*

monella and other Enterobacteriaceae took place frequently, classification would be impossible.

THE RESISTANCE (R) FACTORS

Susceptibility or resistance of serotypes of *Salmonella* to various chemotherapeutic agents and their ability, or lack of it, to produce bacteriocin-like substances have been used extensively as epidemiological markers. In some instances this has led to confusion because of the appearance of multiple resistance in strains isolated from animals that were not receiving all the agents for which resistance appeared.[52, 53] These apparent epidemiologic discrepancies doubtless are due to genetic transfer by conjugation or transduction of episomes that regulate the factors in question.[54-56] In some strains of serotype Typhimurium, resistance to several antibiotics may be transferred as a unit, whereas in others the resistance factors for certain combinations of drugs may be transferred. Further, genetic transfer of resistance from serotype Typhimurium to *E. coli*, and vice versa has been demonstrated.[57]

Because administration of any of the drugs within the range of resistance of a multiply resistant microorganism may result in its selection and dissemination through suppression of the nonresistant flora, some investigators have suggested that it is time to re-examine the entire question of the use of antibiotics and other drugs in the rearing of livestock. The incidence of resistance to tetracyclines has increased rapidly in cultures from both man and animals within the past few years.[58] Multiply resistant salmonellae, many capable of transferring resistance to other microorganisms such as strains of *E. coli*, have been reported in the United States (e.g., References 59 and 60).

Multiple resistance of shigellae to various antibiotics was noted in Japan in 1955[61] and has since been reported in most Enterobacteriaceae and in certain other gram-negative bacteria as well (e.g., References 55 and 61-63). Current knowledge indicates that R factors occur only in gram-negative bacteria. These episomal factors are responsible for development of multiple resistance of microorganisms to antimicrobial agents. Transfer of R factors takes place primarily through conjugation (see F-duction and sexduction, above), but transduction is involved in some instances.[64, 65] Fertile (F+) cells are required, and when Hfr (high-frequency) donor cells are present, recombination and transfer of episomal material proceeds at a rapid rate. Transfer of the episomal R factor material from cell to cell takes place through pili, the presence of which also is genetically controlled. If there is repression of the pilus gene, transfer of drug resistance does not occur. There are at least two naturally occurring R factors having the following effects[65-67]:

	f_1^+R	f_1^-R
1. Suppression of F	+	−
2. Superinfection, immunity to F_1^+R	+	−
3. Superinfection, immunity to f_1^-R	−	+
4. Restriction of phage	−	+
5. Formation of pili (f_1^+, restrict and modify factor)	+	−

Studies indicate that transfer of R factors is mediated by an episomal transfer factor RFT.[53, 55, 68, 69] Transfer of R factors in nature is limited by the rate of conjugation and by the rare occurrence of contact between cells that possess the transfer factor and cells that possess resistance factor. However, when a drug is introduced into a heterogenous population of gram-negative bacteria, selective pressure ("antibiotic pressure") is exerted upon the population, increasing the opportunity for contact between cells that possess the transfer factor and those with R factor. This in turn facilitates the selection and development of multiply resistant strains of bacteria, which then may become predominant. This occurs in hospital and other institutional situations and in animals under analogous circumstances as shown by Anderson.[53] Other transfer factors (TF) mediate transfer of different characters.

This brief description of R factors can be augmented by much additional information available in the literature, and interested readers should examine References 5 and 70–74 in addition to the publications cited in the foregoing paragraphs.

The importance of R factors and the production of multiply resistant strains of various kinds of gram-negative bacteria in hospitals should be obvious. Their importance to veterinary medicine is also clear.[74] Smith,[59] among others, has said that the widespread use of antibiotics in the United States, both clinically and in animal husbandry, probably means that transferable R factors are widespread in gram-negative bacteria in this country and constitute a major public health hazard. He suggests that there be an extensive national study that would examine strains of salmonellae from medical sources and, because of the use of antibacterial agents in animal feeds, strains from farm animals as well. If human carriers are not included in the term "medical sources," representative cultures from carriers should also be examined. The survey should include study of strains of *Salmonella* isolated from animals after transport, in holding pens, and in abattoirs and materials from food-processing plants. The effect of corticosteroids and tranquilizing drugs on the excretion of salmonellae should be investigated further.[75-78]

Anderson[53] reported that "During the winter of 1963–64 an increase in the incidence of antibiotic-resistant strains of *Salmonella typhimurium* (serotype Typhimurium) took place in Great Britain. The commonest phage-type was 29. From the autumn of 1964 onwards, the incidence of type 29 rose more steeply, and the range of drug resistance of the type simultaneously expanded. At first resistant only to streptomycin and sulfonamides, it acquired successively resistances against tetracycline, ampicillin, neomycin and kanamycin, and furazolidone." These resistances all were transferable to *E. coli* strain K12 under experimental conditions. Anderson also showed that the majority of resistant strains of serotype Typhimurium (bacteriophage type 29) of animal origin were recovered from calves on "intensive" farms (in effect, intensive care units), and that epidemics of salmonellosis among such calves often originated from newly purchased animals from particular dealers. Attempts to control the disease were almost exclusively limited to chemotherapy. Anderson[53] stated further that the widespread use of antibiotics for prophylaxis, in particular, promoted the emergence and spread of strains of serotype Typhimurium that carry transmissable R factors. "In 1965 there were at least 590 human cases, with six deaths, due to (bacteriophage) type 29. These infections were almost exclusively of bovine origin." Anderson also suggests that the transmission of *E. coli* strains from animal sources to man probably represents a greater risk than does serotype Typhimurium, since the spread of *E. coli* from animal to man occurs more commonly than the spread of serotype Typhimurium. *E. coli* strains carrying transferable R factors might induce resistance in *S. typhi*. Parenthetically, such *E. coli* strains also might transfer resistance to other salmonellae, to the *E. coli* flora of man (which in turn could result in the occurrence of resistant *E. coli* in urinary tract infections), or to other bacteria in the human intestine. Furthermore, the emergence of resistant strains of *E. coli* pathogenic for animals constitutes a hazard in veterinary medicine and animal health.

Anderson's work demonstrates quite clearly that R factors and indiscriminate use of antibiotics in animal feeds or water are definite hazards to public health. Granted, he mentions prophylaxis in particular, but levels of antibiotics frequently employed for growth promotion may actually be in the ranges that reportedly are used for prophylaxis.

Since about 1950,[79] antibiotics have been added to animal feeds and feed supplements, a practice begun because of their reported (e.g., References 80–83) growth-promoting effect, particularly in poultry and swine. Since that time there has been considerable argument between proponents of this use of antibiotics in feeds and those who oppose the use because of the development of antibiotic-resistant microorganisms, the occurrence of antibiotic residues in the tissues and intestinal tract of animals (e.g., References 53, 83, and 84), and the consequent potential hazard to medicine and public health. A number of investigators (e.g., Reference 84) have shown that there is a gradual increase in resistance of salmonellae in chicks fed antibiotics in their diet. Although the mortality rate in such animals was about one-half that in chicks not receiving the antibiotic, more carriers occurred in chicks that were fed antibiotics.

The significance of residues of antibiotics in meat and edible viscera from animals fed antibiotics is not entirely clear. Some investigators[74] have found no evidence of harm caused by residues of antibiotics in chickens fed low levels and hold that although there may be some hazard from the emergence of resistant salmonellae, the over-all advantages of feeding low levels of antibiotics warrant continuing the practice. Other investigators[74] have argued (a) that caution should be exercised in the use of antibiotics in feeds, (b) that feeding low levels of antibiotics results in the emergence of resistant bacteria, although at a slower rate than when high levels are employed, and (c) that the development of resistance of *Salmonella* in cattle is directly proportional to the amount of tetracycline in the diet.

The various levels of antibiotics employed in feeds and feed supplements need to be defined more clearly. The largest amount to be found in guidelines published in 1952[79] was 40 g per ton, but it has been reported[74] that reduction in cost of antibiotics used for this purpose has led to increases up to 60 to 80 g per ton. Others[74] state that the levels of antibiotics currently employed are as follows:

low level	10 to 49 g per ton (feed supplement)
medium level	50 to 100 g per ton (prophylaxis)
high level	150 or more g per ton (therapeutic)

The suggestion[74] that a surveillance program be instituted to determine whether levels and residues are being kept at safe levels should certainly be acted on. Safe levels should be clearly defined, and where needed, objective studies should be inaugurated to determine what, if any, are safe levels of antibiotics in feeds for animals destined for human consumption. Since different periods of time are required to rid animal tissues of various antibiotics,[74] and low residues in tissues and edible viscera might result in the selection of resistant salmonellae if the organisms are present, the role of residual antibiotics, and products derived from them during catabolism, in developing sensitivities in man should be considered. The suggestion that antibiotics in feeds and water be limited to those that are not as effective in treating clinical disease as those currently employed is untenable, in view of present knowledge of R factors and development of multiple resistance.

A review of the literature on antibiotics in animal feeds and on R factors indicates that, as currently practiced, the additives are causing undesirable changes in the balance between host and pathogen. Additional research is often of value, of course, and the surveillance and other studies mentioned above should be done, but there are ample data now in the literature to support more rigid control of antibiotics in animal feeds and water. An objective re-evaluation of existing data is necessary, since not infrequently two investigators arrive at different conclusions from essentially similar experimental results. Data presently available support the following recommendations.

1. Only truly low levels of various antibiotics should be used in feeds, in water, and in feed ingredients—those minimal amounts sufficient to promote growth. The use of antibiotics should not be a substitute for good husbandry practices.

2. Antibiotics should not be used routinely for prophylaxis of animals.

3. Antibiotic therapy should not be employed in uncomplicated salmonella gastroenteritis in man.

REFERENCES

1. J. Lederberg, *Papers in Microbial Genetics,* Univ. of Wis. Press, Madison, Wis. (1951).
2. E. L. Wollman and F. Jacob, *Sexuality and the Genetics of Bacteria,* Academic Press Inc., New York (1961).
3. J. A. Peters, *Classic Papers in Genetics,* Prentice-Hall, Inc., Englewood Cliffs, N.J. (1959).
4. W. Hayes, *The Genetics of Bacteria and Their Viruses,* John Wiley & Sons, Inc., New York (1964).
5. T. Iino and J. Lederberg, "Genetics of *Salmonella,*" pp. 111–142, in *World Problem of Salmonellosis,* E. van Oye, ed., Dr. W. Junk, The Hague, The Netherlands (1964).
6. A. W. Ravin, *The Evolution of Genetics,* Academic Press Inc., New York (1965).
7. N. D. Zinder and J. Lederberg, "Genetic Exchange in *Salmonella,*" *J. Bacteriol., 64,* 679 (1952).
8. J. Lederberg and P. R. Edwards, "Serotypic Recombination in *Salmonella,*" *J. Immunol., 71,* 232 (1953).

9. T. Smith and A. L. Reagh, "The Non-identity of Agglutinins Acting upon the Flagella and upon the Body of Bacteria," *J. Med. Res., 10* (N.S. 5), 89 (1903).

10. A. Joos, "Untersuchungen über die verschiedenen Agglutinine des Typhusserums," *Zentralbl. Bakteriol., 1. Orig., 33,* 762 (1903).

11. P. R. Edwards and W. H. Ewing, *Identification of Enterobacteriaceae,* 2nd ed., Burgess Publ. Co., Minneapolis, Minn. (1962).

12. J. Marmur, S. Falkow, and M. Mandel, "New Approaches to Taxonomy," *Ann. Rev. Microbiol., 17,* 329 (1963).

13. F. Kauffmann, "On the Transduction of Serological Properties in the *Salmonella* Group," *Acta Pathol. Microbiol. Scand., 33,* 409 (1953).

14. P. R. Edwards, B. R. Davis, and W. B. Cherry, "Transfer of Antigens by Phage Lysates with Particular Reference to the $\underline{1}$, $\underline{w}$ Antigens of *Salmonella,*" *J. Bacteriol., 70,* 279 (1955).

15. N. D. Zinder, "Bacterial Transduction," *J. Cell. Comp. Physiol., 45* (Suppl. 2), 23 (1955).

16. N. D. Zinder, "Lysogenic Conversion in *Salmonella typhimurium,*" *Science, 126,* 1237 (1957).

17. B. A. D. Stocker, "Lysogenic Conversion by A Phages of *Salmonella typhimurium,*" Proc. Soc. Gen. Microbiol., *J. Gen. Microbiol., 18,* IX (1958).

18. H. Uetake, T. Nakagawa, and T. Akiba, "The Relationship of Bacteriophage to Antigenic Changes in Group E Salmonellas," *J. Bacteriol., 69,* 571 (1955).

19. J. Lederberg, "Recombination Mechanisms in Bacteria," *J. Cell. Comp. Physiol., 45* (Suppl. 2), 75 (1955).

20. O. Lüderitz, A. M. Staub, and O. Westphal, "Immunochemistry of O and R Antigens of *Salmonella* and Related Enterobacteriaceae," *Bacteriol. Rev., 30,* 192 (1966).

21. L. LeMinor, "Conversions antigéniques chez les *Salmonella,*" *Ann. Inst. Pasteur, 110,* 562 (1966).

22. M. M. Ball and W. H. Ewing, "Lysogenic Conversion of Somatic Antigens in *Salmonella* Group C," NCDC Publ., NCDC, Atlanta, Ga. (1966).

23. M. R. Escobar and P. R. Edwards, "Lysogenic Conversion of O Antigens of *Salmonella* Group C₁," *Can. J. Microbiol. 14,* 453 (1968).

24. L. S. Baron, W. F. Carey, and W. M. Spilman, "Characteristics of a High Frequency of Recombination (Hfr) Strain of *Salmonella typhosa* Compatible with *Salmonella, Shigella,* and *Escherichia* Species," *Proc. Nat. Acad. Sci., 45,* 1752 (1959).

25. N. D. Zinder, "Hybrids of *Escherichia* and *Salmonella,*" *Science, 131,* 813 1960).

26. L. S. Baron, W. M. Spilman, and W. F. Carey, "Hybridization of *Salmonella* Species by Mating with *Escherichia coli,*" *Science, 130,* 566 (1959).

27. P. H. Mäkelä, "Genetic Homologies between Flagellar Antigens of *Escherichia coli* and *Salmonella abony,*" *J. Gen. Microbiol., 35,* 503 (1964).

28. P. H. Mäkelä, "Inheritance of the O Antigens of *Salmonella* Groups B and D," *J. Gen. Microbiol., 41,* 57 (1965).

29. P. H. Mäkelä and O. Mäkelä, "*Salmonella* Antigen 12₂: Genetics of Form Variation," *Ann. Med. Exper. Biol. Fenn., 44,* 310 (1966).

30. P. H. Mäkelä, "Genetic Determination of the O Antigens of *Salmonella* Groups B (4, 5, 12) and C₁ (6, 7)," *J. Bacteriol., 91,* 1115 (1966).

31. Y. Naide, H. Nikaido, P. H. Mäkelä, R. G. Wilkinson, and B. A. D. Stocker, "Semirough Strains of *Salmonella,*" *Proc. Nat. Acad. Sci., 53,* 147 (1965).

32. M. Sarvas, and P. H. Mäkelä, "The Production, by Recombination, of *Salmonella* Forms with both T_1 and O Specificities," *Act. Pathol., Microbiol. Scand., 65,* 654 (1965).

33. H. Ozeki, B. A. D. Stocker, and S. M. Smith, "Transmission of Colicinogeny between Strains of *Salmonella typhimurium* Grown Together," *J. Gen. Microbiol., 28,* 671 (1962).

34. L. F. Rettger and M. M. Scoville, "*Bacterium anatum*, N.S., The Etiologic Factor of a Widespread Disease of Young Ducklings, Known in Some Places as 'keel'," *J. Infec. Dis., 26,* 217 (1920).

35. P. R. Edwards, "A New *Salmonella* Type Possessing a Hitherto Undescribed Nonspecific Antigen," *J. Hyg., 37,* 384 (1937).

36. P. R. Edwards and D. W. Bruner, "A Description of an Unusual *Salmonella* Type with Special Reference to the Evolution of *Salmonella* Species," *J. Bacteriol., 44,* 289 (1942).

37. G. W. Douglas and P. R. Edwards, "Complex Flagellar Phases in *Salmonella*," *J. Gen. Microbiol., 29,* 367 (1962).

38. A. C. McWhorter and P. R. Edwards, "Unusual *Salmonella* Type with Three 'Normal' Flagellar Antigens," *J. Bacteriol., 85,* 1440 (1963).

39. A. C. McWhorter, M. M. Ball, and B. O. Freeman, "*Salmonella rubislaw* with Three 'Normal' Flagellar Antigens," *J. Bacteriol., 87,* 967 (1964).

40. A. C. McWhorter and A. B. Moran, "*Salmonella lexington* Culture of Complex Antigenic Constitution," *J. Bacteriol., 87,* 1248 (1964).

41. J. Taylor, M. M. Lee, P. R. Edwards, and C. H. Ramsey, "A New Type of Flagellar Variation Associated with New Antigens in the *Salmonella* Group." *J. Gen. Microbiol., 23,* 583 (1960).

42. P. R. Edwards, R. Sakazaki, and I. Kato, "Natural Occurrence of Four Reversible Flagellar Phases in Cultures of *Salmonella mikawashima*," *J. Bacteriol., 84,* 99 (1962).

43. C. C. Spicer and N. Datta, "Reversion of Transduced Antigenic Characters in *Salmonella typhimurium*," *J. Gen. Microbiol., 20,* 136 (1959).

44. H. Hirokawa and T. Iino, "H-antigen of Heterozygous Hybrids between *Salmonella abony* and *Salmonella typhimurium*," *Ann. Rep. Nat. Inst. Genet. (Japan), 12,* 81 (1961).

45. J. Lederberg, "A Duplication of the H_1 (Flagellar Antigen) Locus in *Salmonella*," *Genet. 46,* 1475 (1961).

46. W. H. Ewing and M. M. Ball, "The Biochemical Reactions of Members of the Genus *Salmonella*," NCDC Publ., Atlanta, Ga. (1966).

47. W. J. Martin and W. H. Ewing, "Isolation of *Salmonella* from Foods and Food Products," NCDC Publ., Atlanta, Ga. (1967).

48. *Salmonella Surveillance Report No. 57,* NCDC Publ., Atlanta, Ga. (1967).

49. L. J. Kunz and W. H. Ewing, "Laboratory Infection with a Lactose-fermenting Strain of *Salmonella typhi*," *J. Bacteriol., 89,* 1629 (1965).

50. W. R. Bailey, "Studies on the Transduction Phenomenon. II. The Occurrence of *Salmonella* Transducing Phages in Nature," *Can. J. Microbiol., 2,* 555 (1956).

51. W. R. Bailey, "Studies on the Transduction Phenomenon. I. Practical Applications in the Laboratory," *Can. J. Microbiol., 2,* 549 (1956).

52. E. S. Anderson and N. Datta, "Resistance to Penicillins and Its Transfer in Enterobacteriaceae," *Lancet, i,* 407 (1965).

53. E. S. Anderson, "Facteurs de transfert et résistance aux antibiotiques chez les entérobactéries," *Ann. Inst. Pasteur, 112,* 547 (1967).

54. S. M. Smith and B. A. D. Stocker, "Colicinogeny and Recombination," *Brit. Med. Bull., 18,* 46 (1962).
55. T. Watanabe, "Infective Heredity of Multiple Drug Resistance in Bacteria," *Bacteriol. Rev., 27,* 87 (1963).
56. E. Dubnau and B. A. D. Stocker, "Genetics of Plasmids in *Salmonella typhimurium," Nature, 204,* 1112 (1964).
57. E. S. Anderson and M. J. Lewis, "Drug Resistance and Its Transfer in *Salmonella typhimurium," Nature 206,* 579 (1965).
58. A. C. McWhorter, M. C. Murrell, and P. R. Edwards, "Resistance of Salmonellae Isolated in 1962 to Chlortetracycline," *Appl. Microbiol., 11,* 368 (1963).
59. D. H. Smith, "*Salmonella* with Transferable Drug Resistance," *N. Engl. J. Med., 275,* 625 (1966).
60. F. A. Gill and E. W. Hook, "*Salmonella* Strains with Transferable Antimicrobial Resistance," *J. Amer. Med. Ass., 198,* 1267 (1966).
61. S. Mitsuhashi, H. Hashimoto, R. Egawa, T. Tanaka, and R. Nagai, "Drug Resistance of Enteric Bacteria. IX. Distribution of R Factors in Gram-negative Bacteria from Clinical Sources," *J. Bacteriol., 93,* 1242 (1967).
62. R. B. Williams and W. H. Ewing, "The Susceptibility of *Shigella* and *Escherichia* to Antimicrobial Agents." NCDC Publ., Atlanta, Ga. (1964).
63. S. Vivona, T. T. Minh Ha, F. L. Gibson, and D. C. Cavanaugh, "Antibiotic Sensitivities of Enterobacteriaceae Isolated in Vietnam," *Mil. Med., 131,* 68 (1966).
64. K. Harada, M. Kameda, M. Suzuki, and S. Mitsuhashi, "Drug Resistance of Enteric Bacteria. III. Acquisition of Transferability of Nontransmissable R (TC) Factor in Cooperation with F Factor and Formation of FR (Tc)," *J. Bacteriol., 88,* 1257 (1964).
65. T. Watanabe, H. Nishida, C. Ogata, T. Arai, and S. Sato, "Episome-mediated Transfer of Drug Resistance in Enterobacteriaceae. VII. Two Types of Naturally Occurring R-factors," *J. Bacteriol., 88,* 716 (1964).
66. L. C. Harold and R. A. Baldwin, "Ecologic Effects of Antibiotics," *FDA Papers, 1,* 20 (Feb. 1967).
67. "Focusing on the 'R Factor'," Editorial, *J. Amer. Med. Ass., 200,* 42 (1967).
68. H. S. Ginoza and R. B. Painter, "Genetic Recombination between Resistance Transfer Factor and Chromosome of *E. coli," J. Bacteriol., 87,* 1339 (1964).
69. S. Falkow, R. V. Citarella, J. A. Wohlhieter, and T. Watanabe, "Molecular Basis of R-factors," *J. Mol. Biol., 17,* 102 (1966).
70. N. Datta, "Infectious Drug Resistance," *Brit. Med. Bull., 21,* 254 (1965).
71. E. A. Adelberg and J. Pittard, "Chromosome Transfer in Bacterial Conjugation," *Bacteriol. Rev., 29,* 161 (1965).
72. K. G. Lark, "Regulation of Chromosome Replication and Segregation in Bacteria," *Bacteriol. Rev., 30,* 3 (1966).
73. L. E. Pearce and E. Meynell, "Specific Chromosomal Affinity of a Resistance Factor," *J. Gen. Microbiol., 50,* 159 (1968).
74. *The Use of Drugs in Animal Feeds: Proceedings of a Symposium,* NAS Publ., 1679, Nat. Acad. Sci., Washington, D.C. (1969).
75. S. T. Bowen, J. W. Gowen, and O. E. Tauber, "Cortisone and Mortality in Mouse Typhoid. II. Effect of Environmental Temperature," *Proc. Soc. Exp. Soc. Exp. Biol., 94,* 476 (1957).
76. S. T. Bowen, J. W. Gowen, and O. E. Tauber, "Cortisone and Mortality in Mouse Typhoid. II. Effect of Environmental Temperature," *Proc. Soc. Exp. Biol., 94,* 479 (1957).

77. E. S. Dooley and D. F. Holtman, "Effect of the Administration of Cortisone on the Response of Chicks to the Endotoxin of *Salmonella pullorum*," *J. Bacteriol., 78,* 562 (1959).
78. A. B. Hoerlein and C. L. Marsh, "The Action of Chlorpromazine Hydrochloride in Calves," *Amer. Vet. Med. Ass. J., 131,* 227 (1957).
79. *The Use of Vitamin B₁₂ and Antibiotic Supplements in Livestock Feeding,* A.H.D. Rep. No. 145, U.S. Dep. Agr., Washington, D.C. (1952).
80. H. R. Bird, R. J. Lillie, L. J. Machlin, and C. A. Denton, "Antibiotics in Poultry Nutrition," Reports, IX, *World's Poult. Cong., 2,* 46 (1951).
81. L. J. Machlin, C. A. Denton, W. L. Kellogg, and H. R. Bird, "Effect of Dietary Antibiotic upon Feed Efficiency and Protein Requirements of Growing Chicks," *Poult. Sci., 31,* 106 (1952).
82. R. J. Lillie, J. R. Sizemore, and H. R. Bird, "Environment and Stimulation of Growth of Chicks by Antibiotics," *Poult. Sci., 32,* 466 (1953).
83. J. S. Garside, R. F. Gordon, and J. F. Tucker, "The Emergence of Resistant Strains of *Salmonella typhimurium* in the Tissues and Alimentary Tracts of Chickens Following Feeding of an Antibiotic," *Res. Vet. Sci., 1,* 184 (1960).
84. B. C. Hobbs, J. C. Reeves, J. S. Garside, R. F. Gordon, E. M. Barnes, D. H. Shrimpton, and E. S Anderson, "Antibiotic Treatment of Poultry in Relation to *Salmonella typhimurium*," *Mon. Bull. Minn. Health, 19,* 178 (1960).

Appendix C

The Influence of Sample Size on Analytical Sensitivity in the Analysis of Dried Yolk and Whole Egg for Salmonellae

The results of a study (Silliker, unpublished) in which the sensitivity of salmonella recovery from dried whole egg and yolk was evaluated are summarized.

During the course of one calendar year, the production of dried egg yolk and whole egg in one large processing plant was subjected to salmonella control, samples being withdrawn from each lot of product as follows. Multiple drums from each lot were sampled, a 25-g sample being analyzed from each drum from the lot that was selected for sampling. The number of drums selected for sampling varied according to lot size. But in the sampling plan used, the number of drums from which a sample was to be withdrawn was predetermined. At the time the drums were sampled for the conventional product-control program (involving the removal of 25-g samples for each drum analyzed), a second sample was removed from the same portion of the drum. This sample was used for the ultimate preparation of a 400-g composite sample, representative of the lot. Thus, if five drums where sampled, then 80 g of sample from each of the five drums were used for preparation of the 400-g composite. Similarly, if ten drums were sampled, 40 g of sample were removed from each drum.

As indicated above, the 25-g "drum samples" were analyzed individually, with each being enriched in 250 ml of lactose broth. The 400-g samples were analyzed in 4,000 ml of lactose broth. The same recovery and identification procedures were used on each group of samples.

During the course of this study, 389 lots of egg product were analyzed. Of these, 360 lots were negative for salmonellae, based on the results from both procedures. Sixteen of the lots proved positive both in one or more of the 25-g samples and in the 400-g composite sample. Twelve of the lots were positive in one or more of the 25-g samples but negative in the 400-g composite. One of the lots was positive in the 400-g composite, but each of the 7–25-g drum samples from the lot was negative.

Table C1 gives detailed information on those lots that were positive by both procedures as well as on those lots that were positive in one or more of the "drum samples" but negative in the 400-g composite sample.

Since the total weight of product analyzed by the 25-g procedure varied from lot to lot, a value designated as "average salmonellae per gram" was computed by dividing the number of 25-g aliquots that proved positive by the total weight of sample subjected to the 25-g analysis. This value, for each positive lot, appears in the second and fourth columns of the table.

It will be noted that the lots that were positive by both procedures showed an average level of one salmonella per 70.4 g of product. On the other hand, the 12 lots that were negative using the 400-g procedure but positive in one or more of the 25-g samples, showed an average level of one salmonella per 170 g of egg product.

Statistical analysis of these data indicates that if the average level of contamination within a lot is 0.0057 salmonella per gram or less, the two tests will disagree 95 times out of 100. On the other hand, if the level of contamination within a lot is 0.023 salmonella per gram or more, the two tests will be in agreement 95 times out of 100. These figures assume that if one salmonella is contained in a 25-g sample, enriched in 250 ml of lactose broth, this sample will ultimately yield a positive result.

TABLE C1 Sensitivity of Salmonella Recovery Utilizing 400-Gram Samples versus Multiple 25-Gram Samples

| Lot Samples Positive (400 g) | | Lot Samples Negative (400 g) | |
No. 25-g Samples Pos. No. 25-g Samples Analyzed	Average Salmonellae[a] per gram	No. 25-g Samples Neg. No. 25-g Samples Analyzed	Average Salmonellae[a] per gram
5/14	0.014	1/10	0.004
3/12	0.01	1/8	0.005
3/14	0.012	1/8	0.005
1/2	0.02	1/10	0.004
2/8	0.01	4/12	0.013
5/10	0.02	2/14	0.0057
3/16	0.0075	2/17	0.0047
7/17	0.016	1/6	0.0067
5/9	0.022	1/9	0.004
2/6	0.013	1/9	0.004
2/5	0.016	1/9	0.004
2/6	0.013	1/4	0.01
6/11	0.022		
5/10	0.02		
2/10	0.008		
1/6	0.0067		

54 pos./3,800 g   17 pos./2,900 g

$$\frac{54}{3,800} = \frac{1}{X} \qquad\qquad \frac{17}{2,900} = \frac{1}{X}$$

Average = 1 salmonella/70.4 g   Average = 1 salmonella/170 g

[a] Assuming each positive 25-g aliquot contained a single salmonella.

$$\text{Then: average/gram} = \frac{\text{No. aliquots pos.}}{\text{Total weight analyzed in 25-g aliquots}}.$$

Appendix D

"Wet Compositing" as an Approach to Control Procedures for the Detection of Salmonellae

Silliker (unpublished) has conducted a feasibility study of "wet compositing" as an approach to control procedures for the detection of salmonella. His results are summarized here.

The samples involved in the study were dried foods and feeds that were being analyzed for salmonellae as a part of quality-control programs. All samples were pre-enriched for 18–24 hours at 35°C before subculture. The nature of the pre-enrichment medium varied depending on the nature of the sample. For example, dried milk samples were enriched in water containing brilliant green, dried eggs in lactose broth, rendered animal by-products in lactose broth containing tergitol, and candy in reconstituted nonfat dried milk containing brilliant green.

The pre-enrichment cultures were subcultured in tetrathionate broth containing brilliant green. Approximately half of the samples were subcultured into cystine selenite broth, in addition to tetrathionate broth. The selective broths were incubated at 35°C for 24 hours, at which time the cultures were streaked onto brilliant green, SS, and bismuth sulfite agars.

After incubation, the selective agars were examined for suspect salmonella colonies. These were studied and identified using conventional biochemical and serological procedures.

To evaluate the "wet compositing" approach, incubated pre-enrichment cultures were randomly segregated in groups of 10. Within each group of 10, then, a variety of different samples were represented. Each of the 10 samples was subsequently analyzed according to routine procedures as described above. In the "wet compositing" technique, 1 ml from each of the 10 enrichment cultures was introduced into 10 ml of double-strength selective medium. This "wet composite," representing 10 randomly selected samples, was then analyzed as a single unit, using the procedures described above. Those samples that would ordinarily be subcultured in tetrathionate broth only were "wet composited" only in tetrathionate broth. On the other hand, from those samples that were analyzed using both tetrathionate and selenite broths, "wet composites" were prepared in both selenite and tetrathionate broths. The "wet composites" were then analyzed using the procedures described above.

Table D1 summarizes results obtained in the analysis of 106 "wet composites" representing a total of 1,060 individual samples. Thirty-nine composites were positive for salmonella, 66 negative. In seven instances (designated false negative), one or more of the individual samples comprising the "wet composite" yielded salmonellae. Interestingly, in one case (designated false positive) the "wet composite" was positive for salmonella, even though the analysis of each of the 10 samples comprising the composite was negative.

TABLE D1   Sensitivity of "Wet Compositing" for *Salmonella* Detection

No composites	105
No. composites positive	39
No. composites negative	66
No. false negative composites[a]	7
No. false positive composites[b]	1

[a] False negative indicates failure to isolate salmonellae from the "wet composite," even though one or more of the 10 components was found positive.
[b] False positive indicates "wet composite" was found positive for salmonella, even though each of the 10 components was found negative.